THE MYSTERIES OF TAROT

A WORK OF THE IMAGINATION

KIRSTEN WEISS

MISTERIO PRESS

ABOUT THE BOOK

WHEN TAROT READER HYPERION Night sent his manuscript, *The Mysteries of Tarot*, to his friend to edit, it was an accessible guide to reading Tarot. Hyperion didn't anticipate that his editor's notes would evolve into a murder mystery, or that his friend would go missing. The annotated manuscript eventually made its way back to Hyperion, who forwarded it to the authorities. Now this astonishing Tarot guide is available as a book, complete with the original text, art, and editor's notes.The Tarot guidebook itself contains:

- **Tarot basics**—How to manage all the different interpretations of cards in a spread, how to read Court Cards, and a clear and simple method for dealing with reversals.

- **Detailed card breakdowns**— Keywords, flash non-fiction narratives, and a deep dive into the symbols of each of the 78 cards of the Major Arcana and Minor Arcana.

- **Questions to apply to the cards for transforming your life**—Insightful questions for each card to dig deeper into your Tarot reading practice.

And now it also includes his editor's notes including more esoteric and philosophical interpretations of the Tarot, as well as his notes on the baffling mystery that engulfed him. Gain deep insight from the cards, transform yourself, and solve the *Mysteries of Tarot*.

COPYRIGHT

CONTENTS

INTRODUCTION FROM HYPERION NIGHT

I've been reading Tarot forever and a half. My approach is fairly mundane. I help people figure out where they are, where they'd like to go, and how to get there.

I'm not a psychic. I rely on the Tarot itself for answers. Occasionally, I'll get a flash of intuition, but the cards do the heavy lifting.

Tarot takes us out of our ordinary world. It allows us to look at ourselves from new perspectives. For clients who are ready and willing, a good Tarot reading can help them recognize patterns and habits and break them if necessary.

The likelihood of someone following through on a plan is higher if they come up with it themselves. So after I've read the cards, I help my clients develop an action plan. For this reason, I've included questions at the end of each card description.

Is Tarot magic? A dive into the universal unconscious? Sometimes it feels like both. Other times, I'm not so sure. Even professional Tarot readers like myself can be flogged by insecurities.

When I decided to stitch my thoughts on Tarot into a book, I passed a late draft onto my friend Tom. He's the real deal, a full-tilt mystic. I've seen grown men turn gray at the things he's told them.

And unlike some students of the esoteric, he keeps his feet planted firmly on the ground and knows how to laugh at himself. (My policy is to avoid people who *can't* laugh at themselves — they're the first to go sideways when the world doesn't behave as they expect).

I had to email Tom the manuscript. He was off somewhere in the California woods. I wasn't sure he'd respond, but he did, and he kindly agreed to send me his comments.

When fires started in the areas around his cabin, I emailed to make sure he wasn't in the path of the flames. He didn't write back. That worried me. But being a mystic, ignoring his computer wasn't unusual for him. So I waited.

Two and a half months later, on a Friday night, I received Tom's notes. He knows my habits. It was a time I was practically *guaranteed* not to read them. On the verge of taking off for the weekend, I did no more than send him a brief thank you.

When I returned to my office at Beanblossom's Tea and Tarot on Monday, two men in suits were waiting. One was an arson investigator from Cal Fire. The other was a state police officer.

They told me Tom was missing and under suspicion for starting a forest fire that had burned over a thousand acres. How they'd gotten my name, they wouldn't say.

Tom? An arsonist? It made zero sense. It was *impossible*. Stunned, I answered their questions. The two investigators left dissatisfied.

A slew of clients arrived. There was a minor flood in the tearoom's kitchen. I didn't have a chance to dig into the manuscript until late that night. After reading Tom's notes, I forwarded the manuscript to the investigators, who thanked me politely. I don't think what they found inside made them happy. The easy answer—Tom's guilt—would have been simpler.

I never heard from them again, or from Tom.

Tom is presumed dead. I include his notes in the chapter footnotes. He brings a practical yet esoteric angle to Tarot that I enjoy and respect. Also, I couldn't bear to delete a word. They're *his* words. And I thought that keeping his notes with mine made this book a combination of the practical and the esoteric, the grounded and the whimsical.

I hope you find this guidebook useful, whether you read for yourself or for others.

—*Hyperion Night*

HOW I READ...

IS NOT NECESSARILY HOW *you* should read. Everyone's got their own style. Some insist on shuffling the cards seven times, because seven's a magical number or because it gives the deck a good shuffle. (Guilty. I like the magic seven shuffle). Some will only read with cards that have been gifted to them (nope, not me). But in the context of this book, it probably makes sense to explain my technique.

My favorite deck remains the Rider-Waite-Smith Tarot, first published in 1909 and used as a model for countless decks since. AE Waite and his illustrator, Pamela Colman Smith, were both members of the Victorian magical society *The Golden Dawn* and incorporated esoteric symbolism into their version of the deck.

Each Tarot card has an irritating number of meanings.[1] The Emperor could indicate a need to get organized. Or it could represent working within the establishment, or embodied will, or even daddy issues. Which to choose?

But when the Emperor is joined, for example, in a reading with the Hierophant, (which could mean traditions, authority, institutions, and

---

1. Renaissance Tarot artists drew upon ancient practical philosophy filtered through Neoplatonism, a synthesis of Greek philosophy and mysticism. The practical philosophy of Socrates, the Epicureans, and the Stoics was concerned with how to live life best. Neoplatonists oriented these philosophies toward transcending this life to connect with the Divine.

The Rider-Waite-Smith deck is a reinterpretation of these Renaissance decks. I see a lot of those Neoplatonic ethics—particularly via the Stoics—in its Major Arcana. For example, the four cardinal virtues of Neoplatonism (and Stoicism) were Justice, Courage (the Strength card), Temperance and Practical Wisdom (Prudence, or the World card). These virtues were to act as compass points, guiding the philosopher to a life well lived and/or connection to Source. The idea was that if any path was just, courageous, temperate and wise, it was a good one. -T

the sacred), we get a clearer picture. Certain meanings in these cards overlap. These will be the interpretations I'll focus on.[2]

Then, for example, if the Page of Pentacles, representing a student, turns up, we start to see a relationship—an authority figure/teacher juxtaposed with a student.

In a reading, I'll first tell the client what I'm seeing. After all, they *expect* me to interpret the cards for them. But once my reading is done, I'll let them ask questions, and I'll ask some of my own to help them decide how to move forward.

This is why the ten-card Celtic Cross spread (explained in the next chapter) remains my go-to. It allows the client to look at where they've been, where they are now, what's affecting the situation, and more importantly, where they're headed. Because once you see how your past and present is creating your future, you can *change* it. You can choose a different course. Or if you like where you're going, you can keep doing what you've been doing.

A Tarot reading should be fun, mysterious, and empowering for the client. Ideally, a client leaves my table with a fresh perspective on their

---

2. Moving on, the original Tarot's major arcana (or trumps) used these ancient Greco-Roman symbols alongside Christian allegory to point the way. This combo isn't as odd as it sounds. Neoplatonism was a big influence on the Christian mystics of that time.

I prefer Neoplatonism, but your reading style is more Stoic. Why not look at both interpretations? Maybe the original Tarot decks, though designed as a game, acted as a reminder of how to live one's best life? Maybe the original Tarot wasn't so far from your philosophy on how to read?

Of course, the Major Arcana got a bit muddled through centuries and symbolism. But at its core, Tarot still suggests that the best life is lived through the soul's calling — not the ego's, not society's. And when you're in alignment with soul (or at least when I am), I know how I must act, and that gives me strength and serenity. -T

own lives and maybe with a little awe about how this mysterious deck of cards works.

Readings are odd things. For most people, Tarot readings are unusual, out of the ordinary. And so when we sit down with a reader, we step outside normal reality. And anything can happen.[3]

---

3. I like where you're going with this, but don't be afraid to go deeper. You've read for me. I've watched you read for others, and your approach is useful and genuinely helpful. But there's more. This path doesn't promise a life of ease. We weren't put here for a life of ease. Perhaps that's why so many who have it easy grow so bent.

And no, I'm not just speaking here out of bitter, first-hand knowledge. You know me. You know my family.

But the knowledge in the cards... it changes everything. - T

THE CELTIC CROSS

THE CELTIC CROSS IS a classic, ten-card Tarot spread that allows you to dig deep and see the big picture. The center of the cross, position one, reflects the situation. The card crossing it is (no surprise) crossing the situation, i.e., affecting it somehow. Beneath the situation are your unconscious (position four) patterns. And affecting it from above, your conscious patterns, or the way you're thinking about it (position three). The past influence is behind it in position five, and the immediate future in front of it, in position six.

Next are the cards running along the side of the cross. You (or the client) are represented at the bottom in position seven. Above you is the environment—it could be a person in the environment or just the general state of affairs swirling around your situation.

And then there are those last two cards, nine and ten. I look at nine as the key to the situation, the thing you need to do or change to get the outcome you desire. (Are you sure you desire it? Could your desire itself be blocking you?). If the card is upside down, how can you turn it right-side up?

And then (insert sound of doom or delight here), ten, the final card, the course your situation is currently headed in. This isn't your fate. It's a direction, and you can change it or reenforce it, depending on your ac tions.

How is one supposed to unpuzzle all those cards? Personally, I look for patterns. If I see a mess of cards all pointing in the same direction, then that's the interpretation I'll use. For example, I once was suffering a massive... I'm no psychologist, but let's just call it an anxiety attack and move on.

I was stressed. The situation looked hopeless. And so I drew a Celtic Cross spread. Nine of the cards I drew were from the suit of swords and one card was from cups. The latter was the Seven of Cups, which represents illusion. Now, while Cups tend to represent emotions, Swords are their polar opposite—thoughts. The universe was practically screaming that the drama was all in my head. I didn't even need to analyze the nine Sword cards I'd drawn. (But of course, I did).

The patterns in most ten-card readings aren't usually that glaringly obvious. But the exercise of looking for those patterns—in the cards and in ourselves, can be enlightening.

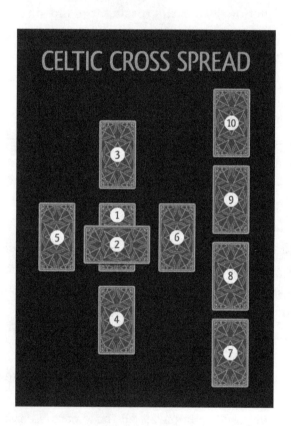

READING COURT CARDS

FOR THE BEGINNING READER, Court Cards are often the most baffling in the deck. Who *are* these people? They're not like the other cards in the deck. What do kings and knights have to do with our past or future? So I wanted to touch on them briefly here.

At their most basic, Court Cards can represent actual people. For example, the Knight of Pentacles may be a conscientious but slow-moving person involved in the situation.

But they also can reflect aspects of the client's personality or their personal qualities affecting the situation. I lean toward the latter approach. When I read for someone, I want them to walk away with actionable ideas. Those could include changes to behavior.

So depending on the position in the reading, a court card could represent:

- Another person involved in the situation or one who will become involved in the future;

- A quality within the client that's affecting the situation;

- A quality within the client that could be used to influence the situation (for better or worse); or

- If reversed, a quality that's being stifled.

To make it easier to remember what their personalities are, the Minor Arcana cards have what are called elemental correspondences. Pentacles are associated with earth, Cups with water, Swords with air, and Wands with fire. Some meanings of these elemental correspondences can be found at the beginning of their chapters. I've found these correspondences can be helpful for understanding and remembering Court Cards, which have their own elemental correspondences. Here they are:

- Pages : earth.

- Knights : fire.

- Queens : water.

- Kings : air.

So a Queen of Swords is a water/air card, and the queen would have a personality to match. For example, this might be someone who can effectively combine intuition (water) with reason (air).

It's useful to consider the positive *and* negative side of these characters. The Queen of Swords is one smart cookie, but she can also be temperamental, judgmental, and acidic. When these cards arise in a reading, ask *how* their energies might be affecting the situation at hand.

READING REVERSALS

WHEN I STARTED READING, I memorized the different meanings of each Tarot card when it appeared upside down (otherwise known as reversals). And then a mentor told me she interpreted reversals as cards with their energies diminished or blocked.

When I applied this methodology to my readings, they got a lot easier. More importantly, they made more *sense*.

Here's what I mean by diminished or blocked.

You draw the Eight of Wands, a card of swift action, and it's upside down. It's next to the Knight of Pentacles, a slow-to-act, thoughtful fellow. In this case, I might read the Eight as a tendency to swift action that should be slowed down.

Or you draw the Fool reversed. Upright, this whimsical card may indicate taking a leap of faith. Reversed, something's blocking that tendency. My next step would then be to look at the surrounding cards, to get a clue as to who or what might be suppressing it, and if it makes sense to d o so.

These aren't hard and fast rules. Sometimes you see a card and you just *know*. And with cards like the Emperor and Empress, which have such archetypal dark and light sides, I might use those dark archetypal meanings in reversals. It all depends on the cards around the reading and the reading itself.

Clear as mud? Good. Let's go.

THE FOOL

THE SPIRIT SEARCHING FOR *experience. Beginnings. Spontaneity. Taking a leap of faith.*

When I was still in the single digits, I thought I was a poet. Hunched in my backyard treehouse, I scribbled verses in a little blank book. And I could rhyme like nobody's business. I'd gotten the whole syllable game down too.

I was having so much fun, I showed my poetry to my kindly, ivory-haired aunt. She was one of the few adults who took an interest in my doings. It was the wrong move. My aunt talked my poems up to my mother.

Things quickly and obviously (even to my young mind), turned patronizing. I was so embarrassed, I didn't write another poem until I was forced to, years later, in some class or other. By that time, I'd lost my knack for rhyming. It's still a struggle.

I wish I'd never shown off my poems. I wish I'd kept writing. But my ego failed me then on both counts. I was young and foolish, but I wasn't acting like Tarot's pure-hearted Fool. I was the Fool reversed. Had I been more "upright," I would have kept on writing despite the smug adults and likely been a better writer today.

Sometimes, you just need to go for it.

The Symbols

The Fool steps toward the edge of a precipice.[1] There are mountains in the background, representing attainment, realization, or a mystical journey. The Fool isn't empty-handed. He's got a bag embroidered with the protective Eye of Horus and carrying universal instinct and memory.

The Fool trusts his instincts. He pursues his dreams even when the world is laughing, because the Fool *believes*.[2]

When the card is reversed, the Fool might be foolishly or naively trusting. After all, he *is* about to step off a cliff. But the little dog by his side barks a warning, so he doesn't fall. As in all reversals, a reversed Fool card could also indicate his energy is being repressed or blocked.

What Does This Card Mean for You?

---

1. Once on a knife-edge cliff in Rhodes, I was the Fool. Behind me was a steep drop to a sand flat. In front and beneath me ran white lines of Mediterranean waves. The wind buffeted me so hard I thought I might fly away. Instead of wisely retreating to safer ground, I stood there, arms high, in a wild ecstasy.

   In that moment, I knew the ancient myths were based in something real and I was a part of them. I could feel all the potential before me, and it made my heart ache with joy. Perhaps my embodiment of the Fool allowed me to touch those archetypes. Or perhaps it was the Fool's potential. -T

2. The Fool stands at zero, nonexistence, just as potential does not exist except as something that could one day exist. Potential is the seed before anything real can manifest, the true beginning before we begin.

   On a different note, the smoke is getting worse from the nearby fires. I'm afraid an evacuation order will come soon. I'm not sure how this will affect my editing, but I'll try to keep up. - T

In life, we need to take risks to move forward. Every journey starts with a step and a risk, a question that won't be answered until you reach the end. This Tarot card asks us to consider how this energy is (or is not) playing out in our lives.

How is the Fool's spontaneous energy affecting the situation at hand? Are you closed up, unwilling to risk, to play, to follow your instincts? Or is something (perhaps ego?) stopping you from taking that leap?

THE MAGICIAN.

The Magician

MANIFESTATION. INTENTION. INSPIRED ACTION[1]. *Using the tools at hand.*

It was not my typical day.

My morning meditation ran away with me, and suddenly the blog post I needed to write was complete in my head. On the way to the tearoom, all the traffic lights in my tiny beach town were green. As I was turning left, I *knew* that the driver beside me was about to swerve into my lane, and I braked. Sure enough, she did. Our cars missed colliding by a hair. In the tearoom parking lot, I found twenty dollars on the pavement.

I was in the zone. And I knew exactly why. Because I was *in the zone.* I felt light and open and in the moment. As within so without. That day, I was the Magician.

I'd like to say I was able to maintain that groove, but I didn't. I'm just not that guy. At least, not usually.

---

1. The Fool is potential, but the Magician acts. Going back to the Neoplatonic virtues, sometimes we fool ourselves that thinking virtuous thoughts is enough. It isn't. Virtue is exercised; it's acted upon. It's a behavior. -T

But the days I am, I don't forget.

The Symbols

The Magician points toward the heavens and the earth, channeling the energies from above and directing them to the material plane. As above, so below.

An infinity sign hovers above his head. He wears an ouroboros—another symbol for the unending—for a belt.

This card is numbered one in the Major Arcana, a number representing beginnings, creation, ideas, and will. It also represents the active, male principal, as well as initiation, inspiration and aspiration—something is about to take form.

All the tools of Tarot—cup, sword, wand, and pentacle—lie before him on his table.[2] Not only is the Magician ready to go, but he's got everything he needs to make things happen—in short, to manifest.

What Does This Card Mean for You?

If this card appears in a reading, consider the situation and examine the tools available and how to utilize them, because now appears to be the time to act. This card asks you to believe in yourself and in the support of the universe.

Are you truly committed to getting what you want? Because commitment is necessary for manifestation.[3]

---

2. FYI, from the Renaissance point of view, the Magician is also a trickster—a street hustler with a shell game. But that isn't the magician Pamela Colman Smith drew. I just think it's interesting. -T

3. To add my mystic's point of view (ha), the magician (and the mystic) see reality differently. They understand that the natural state of the universe is flow, and when they let go of expectations and can live in that flow, magic happens. That's not to say they sit back and do nothing. They act. But they're not attached to the outcome. (Not coincidentally, attachment is usually the thing that gets in the way of achieving the desired outcome. Not only does it cause unhappiness, but it leaves an odor of desperation, which attracts all the wrong thi ngs). -T

THE HIGH PRIESTESS

THE UNSEEN. LIVING WITH the mystery. Sacred knowledge. Intuition and the subconscious. Silence.

"I'm freaking out." My friend Maya dropped into the patio chair opposite me. "It's too much." She clawed both hands through her longish, honey-colored hair as seagulls squawked overhead.

I sipped my tea. "Tell me everything." We hadn't seen each other in ages, and I really wanted to know. Also, it was a gorgeous day at the beach, and I'd snagged a primo table on the restaurant's outdoor patio. Life was g ood.

She edged her chair closer, scraping it across the paving stones. "So there's this guy. I'm pretty sure he's been flirting with me, but I'm terrible at picking up signals. Also, he's not my type, so it would be crazy for me to think what's going on is what I think is going on. But he's really hot and smart, and kind and interesting, and it's driving me crazy."

I laughed. "Bypassing the question about why hot, smart, kind, and interesting is not your type, what's the problem?"

"The problem is my head's about to explode," she said. "Please can I have a reading? Just one card? Please, please, please?"

"Your wish is my command." I pulled my cards from the pocket of my jacket, shuffled, and drew one card, turned it over. It was the High Priestess. "No," I said.

"No, this isn't going anywhere?"

"No, I'm not telling you anything more. You need to live with the mystery."

Her mouth pinched. "What?"

"The mystery is part of the fun," I said. "It's sort of the *point* of new relationships—the excitement of will he or won't he, and figuring out if you're compatible. You need to let this play out, and more importantly, enjoy the play. Things can go either way. The not knowing, the mystery, is the fun of life."

She sat back and folded her arms. "Not helpful."

"Imagine you're living in a rom-com. Whatever's happening now is the set-up for something big. But you have to be *open* to the big. That means staying open to the mystery of now. Just chill."

One of her eyebrows sketched upward. "So your advice is to keep cool and enjoy the ambiguity?"

"Exactly. Well, if *keep cool* means staying present to what is."

Things played out as I predicted. What happened with Mr. Wonderful *was* a set-up for something even bigger. And Maya was ready, because she'd stopped playing mind games with herself, stayed present, and enjoyed the ride instead of second-guessing everything.

The Symbols

The High Priestess sits still and unspeaking between two opposing pillars labeled B and J, *Boaz* and *Jachim*, representing the two pillars of the biblical King Solomon's temple. They don't pull her one way or another. She's not having a panic attack about which pillar she should lean toward. She just *is*, sitting in wisdom.

Other symbols in the card emphasize the concepts of intuition and mystery. The pomegranates on the tapestry behind her likely reference the goddess Persephone, a psychopomp goddess who moved between the underworld (subconscious) and earth (conscious). The High Priestess knows how to tap into the subconscious and apply it in the real world—which happens to be a solid definition of intuition.

Her crown is a disk beneath two horns, similar to the crown worn by the Egyptian goddess Isis, whose cult focused on the celebration of the mysteries.[1]

The Priestess's gown turns watery at the hem, and a crescent moon rises from its folds. Both are symbols of the subconscious.

The word on the scroll she holds is partially hidden. We can only catch a glimpse of the letters TORA, which Arthur Edward Waite of Rider-Waite Tarot deck fame said represented the greater law, the law of the universe. Or is it a Jewish Torah?[2]

What Does This Card Mean for You?

Life is a mystery. It's more rewarding to explore it with a sense of curiosity rather than stewing in anxiety. We don't have all the answers; how boring would it be if we did? And as someone smarter than me once said, it's in the unknown where magic happens.

Are you willing to journey into the unknown?

---

1. Some people believe the High Priestess represents the virtue of practical wisdom, or Prudence, who is frequently depicted holding a book. Since Aristotle said prudence is knowing the right time for the right action (I'm paraphrasing), and this is the beginning of wisdom. This makes Prudence the cardinal virtue. And this flows well with the idea of timing—now is not the time to know. But this virtue may appear in more than one card, such as the World.

   Looking deeper at the card, pomegranates are fertility symbols in many cultures, attributed to Hera and Venus in ancient Greece. The High Priestess may be keeping her secrets, but something is gestating. - T

2. Of course it's the Torah. The Tarot represents two great strains of philosophy from Greece and Jerusalem. -T

THE EMPRESS

PASSIVE ACTION. ALLOWING. NATURE. *Beauty. Fecundity.*

Abigail, my partner at Beanblossom's, dragged me into the woods for a walk. She said I needed to get out of my Tarot cave, and she wasn't wrong. My office has no windows.

Picture the scene. Redwoods and ferns and curling vines encroaching on the winding trail. The butterflies were out in force, black and white, and orange and yellow. Wildflowers sprouted hither and yon. A burbling stream tumbled alongside the path. We crossed simple bridges made of thick planks of wood. High between the branches, smoke from far-off wildfires whitened the sky. But all I could smell was earth and greenery.

Every bend in the trail was a surprise. A very cheerful and very wet shaggy dog materialized. Abigail laughed and let him splatter muddy pawprints on her clothes until the panting and apologetic owner arrived behind his dog.

I was loving it. And then it hit me like last Saturday night. *This* was the Empress.

So much for getting out of my Tarot cave. Tarot had come for *me*. Our woodland adventure *was* the Empress card—the well-groomed trail, the controlled-chaos of the dog...

Symbols

In the Empress card, a pregnant woman lounges between cultivated fields of grain and a wild forest. A heart-shaped stone with the glyph for Venus is carved into her throne, littered with comfy pillows.

The power and authority of the Empress's office is only a thin veneer over her abundant, creative nature. Though nature is chaos, the Empress is not. In front of the wheat field, she symbolizes chaos cultivated to the good—the chaos we need for change, growth and creativity.

Here's the deal. We're creatures of both nature *and* society. Like a farmer's field, we're part chaos, part order. The Empress represents the former and her counterpart, the Emperor, the latter.

In their healthy aspects, the Empress keeps the Emperor from becoming too rulebound, rigid, and tyrannical. The Emperor provides structure for the Empress to blossom. Because like the Empress, we need structure and boundaries (at least *some* boundaries) in order for our personal creativity and purpose to flourish. Whether it's setting word-count goals or deciding only to paint in hues of blue, boundaries can up an artist's game.

But there's a dark side to the Empress.

Chaos can turn dangerous. Nature hits us with a tornado and drops a branch on our heads. Normally, I read reversed Tarot cards as cards with their energies repressed. And that can certainly be true for the reversed Empress. But reversed, she can also be as destructive as the Egyptian goddess Sekhmet or as an evil queen from a folktale. She's the bad fairy, the cruel, dark mother.

What Does This Card Mean for You?

What was the Empress's message for me that day? The walk had unfolded as easily as the blooming wildflowers. Is that what she meant me to understand? Because nature doesn't *work* to make things happen. Nature *is* happening. That's the passive action the Empress represents, that of allowing and being rather than doing and resisting. Did I need to stop trying so hard?[1]

That's the tricky part of Tarot. There are always multiple choices, and in this case, I didn't have any other cards around me to point me in the right direction. Maybe I should have followed the dog.[2]

Nature is abundant, and so are we. Is there something you need to just allow?

---

1. The great French mystic poet Baudelaire once wrote (and I paraphrase —you know the state of my French) that nature is a temple, and its pillars slip us messages in symbols. Sound like anyone we know? Her hidden messages are everywhere. We only need to quiet ourselves and be open to interpreting the repeating symbols and patterns.

   I think my smoky sojourn in the woods whelped me see and hear those messages. Though signs are everywhere, boredom can be mind-expanding. -T

2. Always follow the dog.

   BTW, I had to move. The fires were getting too close to my cabin, and the smoke was unbearable. I've set up new, temporary residence in—don't laugh—the caretaker's cottage on my father's estate. I know, I know. But in fairness, my father was surprisingly decent about it. I expected him to lord it over me. But he just seemed... happy. The prodigal son returns?

   The point is, the move to the estate has slowed me down. I'm only going to get through one of your cards a day.

   On the positive side... I had a heart-to-heart with my sister for the first time in years. She dropped by the cottage with one of her dogs and was soon bossing me around and getting the place in order. I think I needed it. -T

THE EMPEROR

AUTHORITY. SELF-DISCIPLINE. FATHER ISSUES. *Organization and structure.*

My dad doesn't understand me.

Trite, no? But it's true. He's a scientist for a government lab so well-known you must have heard of it, though I'm forbidden from mentioning the name. He's a top dog, a big poobah. And he didn't get there by frittering his days away dreaming about magic and the subconscious and the esoteric meanings of Tarot.[1]

Even at home, he was working. He had a lab in the garage for his own private experiments. It was the full mad scientist's kit, though his was organized to terrifying precision. Given the things he worked on, he had to be precise.

I can't count the times he looked at me like I was one of his experiments—a curiosity to be puzzled out, a phenomenon to be dissected. He's cold. Unyielding. And he never let me get away with any crap. But

---

1. You think you've got daddy issues? My father's one of the richest
   · men in America. And he didn't get that way through clean dealing
   and kindness. Why do you think I've been living in the woods? - T

he also provided me with a stable childhood and room to grow into the person I was meant to be.

He reminds me a *wee* bit of my business partner, Abigail. When I first met her, she was armed with a full-color business plan and five years' worth of projected financial statements. I had... some vague ideas for a Tarot studio.

She seriously annoyed me. But a part of me felt comforted by her schedules and plans. They felt familiar.

In the end, neither of our plans (and I use the word *plans* loosely in reference to myself) worked out the way we expected. (Our realtor died, then we learned he was a conman. It was very high drama).

But I have to admit, Abigail's budgets and worksheets have come in handy. Not that I *follow* them. But when things go wrong, or when I'm unsure, I do pull them out and let them guide my decision.

If Abigail ever reads this book and finds out, I'll never hear the end of it.

The point is, though I'm not the most structured or organized, there are times when those Emperor traits come in handy. The dance between creative spontaneity and structure is one I'm still learning. But it's worth the occasional misstep. This is a card of self-discipline, and the Emperor at his best provides us with a kingdom to flourish in.

The Symbols

The Emperor sits on his solid symmetrical throne and stares squarely at the reader. There's no nonsense here. His stone throne is decorated with rams' heads, symbols of authority and leadership.

He holds other symbols of his authority as well—an orb and a scepter shaped like an Egyptian ankh, the latter also representing eternal life. There's no escaping these archetypes. But when his dark side comes out, he becomes the destructive, tyrannical father.[2]

---

2. This is essentially the difference between the Emperor who turns his power outward versus inward. In his positive state, the Emperor is about self-discipline, authority over oneself. But when he attempts to discipline others, exert authority over others, things go wrong. - T

What Does This Card Mean for You?

When this card appears in a reading, it asks how the energies of the Emperor might be at play (or might need to be at play) in the situation. Should the issue be approached in a logical, orderly, and structured fashion?

THE HIEROPHANT

TRADITION. AUTHORITY. INSTITUTIONS. THE *Sacred*. A *Teacher*.

Among Tarot readers I know, The Hierophant is hands-down the most hated card in the deck. The Death card? No problem. That just means something has already died. The Devil? Take your blinders off and handle it. But the Hierophant, representing authority and tradition?

Bleeaah.

Tarot readers tend to be a bit outside the mainstream—at least the ones I like. And that means we're anti-establishment. Down with the Man!

And in the oldest Tarot decks, the Hierophant card was the *Pope*. Half the readers I know are pagan. A Pope card just isn't relatable to a lot of people. Changing the card to the Hierophant might have taken certain traditional religious elements out of the equation, but the negative attitude towards the card has stuck.

And it's totes unfair.

Not all traditions or institutions are good (obvs). But many of them developed because they *do* help us navigate this nasty, brutish, and short thing called life.

In today's upside-down world, I find myself longing for more tradition, for rituals, for the wisdom of the past. (Authority can still stick it though).

I'm not saying the past was all good, but neither is the present. And there are some traditions that can help guide us on our way to enlightenment. Or at least to a better life. Like:

- Traditions regarding life's changes.

- Traditions about the changing seasons and holidays.

- And traditions about how we treat each other.

As to authority and institutions, as much as I like to thumb my nose at both, I'm over-the-moon I don't live in an anarchic society. It's *nice* to know that when I turn the tap clean water will come out, that there will be food in the stores, and my odds of getting robbed on the way to those stores is minimal.

The Symbols

In this card, a high-ranking religious figure blesses (or instructs?) two tonsured priests. He holds a triple cross and wears a triple crown. Take your pick as to what the threes represent—a vicarage over heaven, earth and hell? Mind, soul, and body? Lower, middle, and upper world? Whatever you choose, both cross and crown represent traditional authority.[1]

What Does This Card Mean for You?

When this card appears in a Tarot reading, it challenges us to figure out how the Hierophant's energies are working in our lives. Is there traditional knowledge out there that can help with the situation?

---

1. Back to our ancient Greek ethics, the Stoics believed in order to follow the path, it helped to find a teacher. The answers may be within, but a good mentor can help us find and interpret them. I resist authority figures too. Maybe it's why you and I get along so well? - T

THE LOVERS

"No." He shook his silvery head. "Pleasure and happiness aren't the same."

The man was an old-school psychologist, researching the use of Tarot as a Rorschach test with a Jungian twist. He was interviewing me in my office over cups of Tarot tea.

I was taking the opportunity to interview him right back. I slouched in my high-backed wood and velvet chair, tabby at my feet. "Pleasure and happiness seem pretty darn close."

He grimaced and brushed a crumb of scone from the crimson tablecloth. "It's a common mistake. There's nothing wrong with pleasure, per se. But when we confuse pleasure with happiness, we lose happiness. We get pleasure from eating the junk food, lounging in front of the TV, scrolling on social media. These types of activities give us hits of dopamine."

"But?"

"But chasing that high doesn't lead to happiness. In fact, the very things that can give us pleasure, can lead to long-term *unhappiness*. Too much pizza makes us fat. Television dulls our brains. Time on social media turns to doom scrolling and comparisons with others."

"And happiness?"

"Ah." He braced his elbows on the arms of the thronelike chair and steepled his fingers. "Happiness is derived from three things: one's spiritual life, putting in time with people we care about, and meaningful work—work that serves others."

Was that why I loved my work? I felt my readings were of service. I got to spend time with people I liked. *And* there was a spiritual component.

"At a physiological level," he continued, "these three activities stimulate our brains. On a metaphysical level, they bring meaning. Pleasures like drinking wine and vegging on the couch do the opposite. The pleasure fades and eventually make us miserable."

"It seems you're saying happiness comes from making choices that benefit us in the long term, rather than from short-term fun."

He shot me a satisfied smile. "Exactly."

"You're talking about the Lovers card."

The Symbols

Older versions of this card depict the mythological hero Heracles faced with two women representing virtue and pleasure. Since Heracles was also renowned for being quite a player, the obvious choice for him should have been pleasure.

But this being a heroic tale, Heracles chose virtue instead. He took the path of long-term happiness over short-term fun. [1]

At a deeper level (and in the ancient texts there's nearly always a deeper level), this isn't a mere morality tale. Virtue can't exist without choice. Following orders, doing what you're forced to do, isn't particularly virtuous, even if the orders themselves may be. We need the freedom to choose the opposite for virtue to have any meaning at all.

The Rider-Waite-Smith deck reimagined this card from a more Judeo-Christian perspective, placing our lovers in the Garden of Eden with an angel poised above them. Arthur Edward Waite gave this card his own twist, rejecting the vice/virtue choice for a symbolic representation of higher human love[2]. After all, Adam and Eve are a *couple*, an allusion to love and relationships.

Yet the artist, Pamela Colman Smith, was careful to include imagery regarding choice. The Tree of Knowledge of Good and Evil stands behind Eve, and the Tree of Life is behind Adam. In Eden, Adam and Eve were

---

1. I like that you brought in the ancient Greeks again. And you're right. There can be no virtue without choice. But I think you missed the obvious here. Love and choice. It's no accident these two concepts are combined because love IS a choice.

   Of course, when I write "love is a choice," I don't just mean romantic love. But we both know people who've confused infatuation for love. And when that burning, yearning, passionate feeling dies, as it always will, someone walks away thinking the love is gone when really it's just the chemical rush of infatuation that's vanished. And instead of making the choice to love, to reach for something deep and true and lasting, they leap into the next infatuation and inevitably suffer the same disappointment. -T

2. The Greeks called it pragma—the love that continues beyond passion and infatuation and endures. But they defined other types of love too. Agape—selfless, altruistic, and unconditional. Philia—affection-ate love you have for a friend. Philautia—self-love.

   Whatever you choose, choose love. -T

perfect innocents. But without the knowledge of good and evil, they had no real choice, and no real freedom.

What Does This Card Mean for You?

In every moment we have a choice—fleeting pleasure or true happiness. This card asks us to consider where we're putting our energy. Will we be happier and more fulfilled if we make a shift?[3]

---

3. Apropos of nothing, there's a crow's nest outside my front door, and the crows argue constantly. It was massively irritating, until I realized I was being triggered by echoes of my past. I can't escape my family dynamics. However, while I couldn't choose my family, I did choose to be here. Maybe coming home was a mistake. The easy path usually is, isn't it? -T

THE CHARIOT

CONSCIOUS CONTROL. INNER CONFLICT. *Willpower. Success.*

Have you ever struggled with a bad idea? Wanted to do something you knew you shouldn't do?

Of course you have. We *all* have.

That's the Chariot.

Or that's *Plato's* chariot. The Tarot came to us via Renaissance Italy, which was obsessed with the ancient Greeks in general and with Neo-Platonism in particular. The chariot card is another one of the more obvious archetypes from that realm.

In Plato's description of one of Socrates' dialogues, Socrates described the human soul as a charioteer steering two horses of different natures. One horse is light and of noble breed. The dark horse is lustful, irrational, and generally that voice in your head telling you that yes, you can get away with it *just this once*. The charioteer himself knows what's right and wrong. He's got reason and knowledge on his side. But steering those troublesome horses can still be a challenge.[1]

The Symbols

Pamela Colman Smith replaced the horses with sphinxes in her version of the card. She probably didn't do it to hammer home the Greek-myth element.[2] Sphinxes, with their combination of human and animal attributes, also represent the connection between the subconscious and the conscious minds. This in turn reflects back on the inner conflict that can develop within us.

But chariots, used in war and triumphal processions, are also symbols of victory. This card can, therefore, also represent success.

What Does This Card Mean for You?

It takes strength to control a chariot, whether the horses are pulling against each other or no. The first step is understanding what direction you want to go in, and from there, understand how you might be standing in your own way. What must you do to see this journey through to the end?

---

1. The Greek philosophers would go deeper here. Plato believed the soul or psyche had three parts, represented by the charioteer and the two horses. One horse is mortal, the other immortal. Either horse can lead him to the right or the wrong path. This is important. One is not better or worse. The point is not to subdue one of the horses; it's to achieve harmony. He must use his reason to harness their impulses if he's going to follow the gods into the heavens.

   But though the gods have two immortal horses to keep them aloft, the charioteer is burdened with one mortal horse, which keeps trying to pull him back to earth. The charioteer keeps catching glimpses of the truth and beauty beyond this world, but the mortal horse yanks him away from that vision. If he fails at piloting the horses successfully, he'll fall. But the longer he stays up, the less painful and permanent the fall will be.

2. She wasn't the first to use sphinxes in this card. You can find the same in Oswald Wirth's Tarot des Imagiers du Moyen Age from 1899.

STRENGTH

INNER STRENGTH. COURAGE. FORTITUDE. *Compassion.*

"For in the same degree in which a man's mind is nearer to freedom from all passion, and in the same degree also is it nearer to strength: and as the sense of pain is a characteristic of weakness, so also is anger. For he who yields to pain and he who yields to anger, both are wounded and both submit." — Marcus Aurelius, *Meditations*, from the George Long translation, 1862.

I know. It's always a little suspicious when someone starts a personal essay with a quote. But since so much Tarot symbolism comes from the ancient Greeks and Romans, I thought going back to basics might help illuminate the Strength card. Because the above quote by the Roman Emperor and Stoic Aurelius is about both the lady *and* the lion.

The lion in this card echoes the old Roman story of the lion with a thorn in its paw. It roared and stalked about and terrified the local villagers. Until one day, a shepherd named Androcles found himself—quite by accident—alone in a cave with the beast.

Androcles could have run (and likely gotten eaten). But despite his terror, he remained calm, studied the lion, and realized it was in pain. Once the shepherd removed the thorn, the lion was so grateful he became Androcles's BFF.

We can apply this lesson to people. Because let's face it, when have you *ever* calmed down a situation by losing your temper? I'm sure it *has* happened in the history of the world, but it's rare. The strength to stay calm and to show love is much more likely to tame the beasts around us.

But we can also apply this to our inner lives. Anger and fear make us weak. It's love that makes us strong. We've all got lions rampaging inside us—wounds of memory that manifest in hatred, fear, desire. Showing kindness and patience to the dark parts of ourselves is the quickest way to tame them.

The Symbols

A maiden holds open a lion's mouth like a circus lion tamer. Like the Magician, an infinity sign hovers above her head. It's a reminder that lions will always be inside us, and the work of taming them is eternal.[1]

Flowers representing love and spirituality garland her head and waist. A mountain, a symbol of attainment, rises in the background.

---

1. The Neoplatonists believed we were put here to transcend the limitations of this world and experience the Divine. The Stoics, whose philosophy Neoplatonism syncretized, believed we were put here to fully experience this world and to be the best humans possible. These two competing strains of philosophy struggle against each other to this day, appearing in various modern ideologies. Would it shock you to learn I, the man you call the "mystic in the woods," fall into the Stoic camp on this issue?

Of course, aetheists might say we weren't "put here" at all.

The problem is that both philosophies can fall prey to narcissism and authoritarianism. They both struggle against the same poisoned apple—the shadow side of human nature. The Strength card is their answer to this—acknowledge that darkness, have compassion for ourselves, and through that control our darker impulses. But that infinity sign implies the struggle is eternal and transcendence a pipe dream—not very Neoplatonic! -T

What Does This Card Mean for You?

This card asks us which lions are rampaging and affecting the situation. And it shows us a solution. Like Androcles we can study what's really going on inside (and outside) and react with love. That might take the greatest courage of all.

What (or who) do you have to forgive?[2]

---

2. I'd take this deeper. The lion is our shadow—the dark parts of ourselves we don't want to admit exist and that we feel shame about. But when those dark emotions arise, we fight them, resist them, tell ourselves we shouldn't be feeling them, and that just feeds the beast, making it stronger.

   But if we acknowledge what we're feeling and focus on how it feels inside of us (a prickling in our chest, tightness in our throat), we can sit with it. And as we do, the feeling will dissipate and lose power. We'll understand it's just a feeling, and whatever triggered that feeling will have less power over us.

   As I was editing your card, the crows were making a tremendous noise. I hurried outside thinking the nest was under attack. The smallest crow fluttered on the ground, and the other crows were harrying it. It must have been kicked from the nest.

   I knew the feeling. Needless to say, I rescued the crow. It's now sleeping in a nest of towels beside my laptop. -T

THE HERMIT

TRUTH. WISDOM. INNER GUIDANCE. *Contemplation.*

I've been thinking a lot lately about what's real. If you follow the media, it's getting harder and harder to know what to believe.

One "expert" says X. The other says Y. The expert I believe is the one I *want* to believe, the expert that confirms my biases. But of course, that doesn't make that person—or me—correct. So how can we find the truth?

We can't rely on overnight experts, glibly confident personalities without real depth or knowledge. The Hermit wouldn't do so, because he knows that information alone isn't truth. It's only data, and data is prone to interpretation and misinterpretation.

Consensus isn't necessarily truth either. People get to a consensus through compromise. What they agree upon *could* be true. But it also could be groupthink gone wrong.

So the Hermit goes his own way. He journeys through rocky terrain, lantern held high, seeking the truth in the darkness, and knowing that information is mediated through wisdom. The quest for truth requires commitment, it requires stress-testing one's beliefs, and it requires us to accept sometimes going it alone.

Truth can be a solitary quest down darkened paths, disconnected from the crowd. It can be lonely, but I think it's worth it.

The Symbols

An old man, a symbol of wisdom, stands on a dark mountaintop[1] representing attainment. But he isn't just any old man. He's a hermit, an icon of solitude and self-determination. He lights the way with his lantern, lit by a star.[2]

What Does This Card Mean for You?

The Hermit card asks us to question, well, everything. What "truths" are you going along with because everyone else does? Is it time to take the journey and dig deeper?[3]

---

1. At the base of a mountain, our view is narrow, obstructed by the mountain itself, by the trees, by the brush. But as we rise, the mountain tapers, becomes narrower, and our vision expands to the horizon. Sometimes we need to climb to the top—for all its struggles to get there—to see the reality of the big picture. And sometimes we just need to get away. -T

2. I suspect you want me to talk about that star in his lantern, but the symbolism can go in so many directions as to be nearly useless. On the other hand, the symbolism of the mountain interests me. - T

3. This cottage is way too close to my father's house. He stopped by yesterday. I'm not sure what good-old pops wanted, but he'd been drinking. He sat and rambled about nothing while the crows made their racket outside, and then he left. I think we were both relieved when he did.

   Coming here was a mistake. At least Charles and Adelaide have been steering clear since her first and last visit last week. My brother and sister are living at the mansion with my father's newest wife, Joan. I met Joan only once, at their wedding. This should tell you everything you need to know about my family. Do you still wonder why I became a hermit in the woods? - T

WHEEL OF FORTUNE.

THE WHEEL OF FORTUNE

DESTINY. TRANSFORMATION. LUCK. SPIRITUAL *alchemy*. A *turning point*.

There's an old Chinese proverb about a farmer. You've probably heard it before. The farmer and his son had a horse that helped them plow the fields. One day, it ran away.

"Alas, what a terrible misfortune!" his neighbor said.

"Maybe so," the farmer replied. "We will see."

Days later, the horse returned with three wild mares behind it.

"What wonderful fortune!" his neighbor said.

"Maybe so," the farmer replied. "We will see."

A few days later, the farmer's son broke his leg trying to tame one of the mares.

"Alas, what a terrible misfortune!" his neighbor said.

"Maybe so," the farmer replied. "We will see."

The next week, the Chinese army came through the village looking for recruits. When they saw how badly the farmer's son was injured, they didn't draft him.

"What wonderful fortune!" the neighbor said.

"Maybe so," the farmer replied. "We will see."

The Symbols

Wheels represent cycles and motion. They revolve around a center pivot, a turning point. And the wheel on this card has its own rising and falling action, turning counterclockwise, against expectations. A snake slides down on the left, an Anubis-type figure rises on the right. And above it all sits a sphinx, representing ancient wisdom and acting as an equilibrium.

There are a lot of theories about what the winged creatures—eagle, lion, bull, and man—in the corners of the card represent. I won't go into them all, because I'm not sure they matter. What matters is the *motion*.[1]

I prefer to think of the creatures[2] astrologically, as the four fixed zodiacal signs, fixed points in the heavens upon which the universe (seemingly) revolves. It's the macro version of the wheel. As the universe rotates, so does the wheel, and like the universe, there's a hub, a fixed, still center.

On the wheel are four alchemical symbols: sulfur for expansion, mercury for integration, salt for contraction, and water for dissolution. Alchemy is at root a chemical reaction. It's transformative. Our reactions to what's happening around us can be transformative too, if we're mindful.

---

1. What matters is the matter, ha ha. These four compass points represent this world. The wheel spins within it. - T

2. What's really interesting to me is the creatures are all reading books, which symbolize knowledge, wisdom, and memories. I prefer to think they're reading mystery novels though, LOL. The point is, they're indifferent to the spinning of the wheel, just as fortune is indifferent to its impact on us. -T

THE MYSTERIES OF TAROT

THE MYSTERIES OF TAROT

There's opportunity for personal and spiritual growth in these ups and downs, *if* we can find our own fixed, still center.[3] That's what the Wheel of Fortune calls us to do. Not to let what's happening around us shake us, but to be like that farmer, unmoved by good or bad fortune.

What Does This Card Mean for You?

Mindfulness matters. Wheels can turn quickly, and opportunities come and go. How can you go inward and find your still point?[4]

---

3. The early Tarot cards drew on the concept of the goddess Fortuna, who dispensed good and bad luck at random. Stoicism and Neoplatonic ethics suggest it's better to learn from these wins and losses, rather than dwell on them. The Stoics also believed the ups and downs of Fortune provided opportunities for growth.

   The philosopher Seneca wrote, "[The philosopher's] course will not be straightforward; he must go upwards and downwards, be tossed about, and guide his vessel through troubled waters: he must make his way in spite of fortune: he will meet with much that is hard which he must soften, much that is rough that he must make smooth. Fire tries gold, misfortune tries brave men." (On Providence 5.9, 1900 translation by Aubrey Stewart). Note the chemical/alchemical metaphor? In the end, we can't control fortune. We can't control the world around us. We can only control our own actions and reactions. - T

4. And sometimes just when you think you're in the absolutely wrong place, you discover everything is right. I had the most vivid vision of my life while editing this page. A crack of thunder shook the cottage. I walked outside and from the thundercloud looming over the oaks emerged a ball of fire with the four, four-faced angels of Revelations. You remember them from Ezekiel's vision? One face was human, one an ox, one a lion, one an eagle. The fire separated into four wheels. The angels flew off with them in the four cardinal directions.

   For whatever reason, being here at the old place with so many memories—hard as they are—is the right time for transformation. - T

JUSTICE

JUSTICE. BALANCE. DOING THE *right thing. The spiritual consequences of our actions.*

Valentine couldn't quite meet my eye. "The thing is, we have a *connection.*" She shifted in the high-backed, red velvet chair.

On the driftwood altar, my tabby, Bastet, growled. He didn't believe it either.

Love and money are the two top reasons people come to a Tarot reading for insight. Or at least I like to *think* they're looking for insight. They're frequently just hoping to hear what they want to hear.

Valentine wanted to hear that an affair with her hot co-worker was in the stars. I doubted it, but she'd come for a reading, not my personal opinion.

"Let's see." I turned over the card. *Justice.*

She propped her elbows on the table, the motion rumpling the crimson cloth. "What's that have to do with love?"

"It has to do with cause and effect," I said. "When you do the wrong thing, the outcome won't be one you like."

"But what if it's the right thing?"

"This card is packed with ancient Roman god energy, and they don't mess around. There's no gray area here."

Valentine left dissatisfied, and I didn't see her again. I did hear from the friend who'd referred her. She'd gone ahead with the affair, and the whole thing had blown up in her face. She'd lost her husband *and* her new love.[1]

But I'd warned her about the gods. The ancient myths are brutal, no-nonsense, take-no-prisoners. Oedipus didn't get a pass on killing his father and marrying his mother because he didn't *know* they were his mother and father. The gods took him down anyway.

And sometimes that's life. Doing the right thing can hurt, but the long-term effect of doing the wrong thing is much, much worse.

The Symbols

Cause and effect are implicit in the concept of justice. We're judged on our *actions*. Like the High Priestess, Justice sits between two pillars, but here, the symmetry is all about balance.

Justice holds the traditional symbols of justice—scales, representing judgment, and a double edged sword that both executes the law and defends. The sword is upraised, symbolizing victory. You can't escape justice.[2]

What Does This Card Mean for You?

---

1. Fun fact: Justice corresponds to Libra, ruled by Venus, which puts the focus on relationships. So your anecdote is perfect. On a darker note, it doesn't FEEL like people can't escape justice. Or maybe they only escape lower-case justice, not upper-case Justice? - T

2. I'm surprised you didn't mention that Justice was one of the four Greek virtues, and probably the most important. If you don't do the right thing, everything else is meaningless. And the Stoics believed the right thing included fighting for your ideals, because one person can make a difference.

   Maybe that's where I've fallen short. I've told myself my life of isolation was a way to get closer to the Divine. But has that been a cop-out? Have I been hiding from my responsibilities? Even on my father's estate, I'm still hiding, pretending everything's okay between my family and me. But it's a lie. Will Justice come for me? - T

This card asks you to consider how the concept of justice is playing out in your life. Are you doing the right thing?

THE HANGED MAN

SURRENDER. ACCEPTANCE. SUSPENSION. SACRIFICE. *Letting go.*

A friend of mine—we'll call her K—came to me in dire emotional straits. She was stuck. After flying high, in the zone, feeling one with light and love and bliss, she'd hit a block and come crashing down.

For weeks, all she'd wanted to do was cry. But she'd kept the crying private. Now all she could think about was everything that was wrong with her life. All her failures. All her lack. And the fact that she'd been in such an amazing mood for months previously just deepened her current p ain.

"I *know* the joy is there, inside me," she told me across my reading table. "But I'm stuck. I just can't seem to reach it. I've been meditating. I've been letting go—or at least trying to. What else can I do? How can I move forward? Because right now all I feel is blah, and I *hate* it."

She was in an existential Hanged Man period, and a particularly rough one on the emotions.

"Have faith in the process," I told her. "Believe this period of introspection, meditation, and withdrawal is going to end. And once it does, it'll bring a spiritual reward."

I could tell she *wanted* to believe me, but she couldn't quite bring herself to do it.

"Honestly," I said. "Just stop trying and trust something good is on its way. You may as well. The trying isn't working, and it's giving you even more stress."

She sighed. "I'll try."

I shot her a look.

She laughed. "I'll *be*."

I sympathized with her challenge. The Hanged Man can be angsty.

The card suggests we surrender to what is and let go of what's holding us back. Those things could be external, like people or circumstances, or internal, such as wants and beliefs. Sometimes the wanting can get in the way of the getting, and the quickest way to get where you want to go—or just to move on and be happy—is to stop struggling.

The Symbols

In the card, a sacrificial figure hangs upside down from a living tree. His expression is relaxed. The action is clearly stopped. The Hanged Man isn't going anywhere, and he appears content with that, indicating the stopped action is the right thing to do at the time. This card represents a period of withdrawal.

The Hanged Man isn't struggling against his bonds; he's "going with the flow." K's stuckness was the right thing for her at the time, if she could just accept it.[1]

K returned a month later with a big smile on her face. "You were right," she said. "Something *has* changed. I'm still not sure what it is, but I know I'm on the right path."

What Does This Card Mean for You?

---

1. In the Renaissance period, traitors were hanged upside down. This card may have originally been a warning against betrayal. Like most, I prefer the more modern interpretation. Or, taking your more positive, internal-growth spin, maybe it's a warning against betraying our ideals? And now I'm projecting. - T

Sometimes the path to transformation involves making the best of tough situations by accepting and meditating on them. What do you need to accept?

DEATH

LETTING GO OF ATTACHMENTS. *Natural and inevitable change.*

Edie grimaced. "So. There's this guy." She gulped from her champagne glass. Around us at the wine bar, people laughed and mingled.

I grinned. I like Edie. She's kind, smart, and honest. And she deserved some fun. "Tell me *everything*."

She drew a deep breath. "For a lot of very logical reasons he isn't Mr. Right. But I'm kind of okay with Mr. Right *Now*. In fact, I'm more than okay. I can't stop thinking about this guy. I play it cool on the outside, but he's knotted me up but *good*."

"And the problem is?"

"It's gotten ridiculous. I think I've become attached to a fantasy in my head, not the real man. I'm afraid I'm blowing this up into something it's not. I'm not even sure how he feels about me."

Edie was in a better place than she thought. She knew the tricks she was playing on herself, just not how to release her attachment to her fantasy.

Here's the weird thing about attachments though. Deep down, a lot of us believe that if we give them up, we won't get what we want. But the

THE MYSTERIES OF TAROT

truth is, if we're attached, we end up with this needy and desperate vibe which ensures we *don't* get what we want.

I pulled out my Tarot deck and drew a card. "Let's see what Tarot says."

She leaned forward eagerly. I placed a card on the black quartz bar and turned it over. *Death.*

She cursed. "Seriously?"

"Chill. This card is about letting go. Death represents releasing attachments. Change is coming, whether you like it or not. So let it happen and let go of this guy. Walk away. Once you let him go, the path will be cleared for something better. Trust me."

She gave me an uncertain look, and I couldn't blame her. I don't like change. In this, I'm *pretty* sure I'm not alone.

Change is chaos and uncertainty, and I'd much rather stick with the comfortable known. But life is change. And if we try to keep the status quo, hold on to our attachments and expectations about what we think *should* come next, we end up making things worse.

And if you *can't* let change happen... you end up with the Tower card. In other words, change is going to happen even *more* painfully and dramatically, in Tower-like fashion.

Edie did manage to let her fantasies go. And after a lot of introspection, she let the guy go too. And then, of course, she *did* find Mr. Right.

The Symbols

The good news is Death is an ending and a beginning. The white rose on Death's banner symbolizes internal purity and peace, as well as freedom from lower forms of desire, hinting at the path to something new.

If you look carefully at this card, you'll see in the background the sun rising between two towers. The towers are gateways, symbolizing transition. There's more to come, a new beginning... *if* you let go of expectations and embrace the change.

What Does This Card Mean for You?

When you get this card, don't freak out. Just ask yourself what beliefs, ideas, and expectations you're holding onto, and what maybe you need to let go of. What is it costing you to hold on?[1]

---

1. Continuing with the philosophy theme, the Stoics believed it was important to keep one's death front and center to remind us to appreciate life. It's called momento mori.

But sometimes the Death card does mean death. There was another storm last night. Lightning struck the tree outside the cottage—the tree with the nest. My Oswald is the lone survivor. I was sure the strike would set the woods on fire, but the rain had extinguished the flames before the fire department could arrive. Considering how dry everything is, it's more than a little disturbing it took them nearly forty minutes to get to me. They told me they were short-staffed—everyone's further north fighting the fire that chased me from my home. FYI, it looks like my old cabin may be gone. - T

TEMPERANCE

Detachment. Balance. Synthesis. Patience.

I hate, hate, *hate* that Temperance is my birth card, number fourteen. I'm not temperate. At *all*.

Offered an extra slice of pie, I'll take it. Then I'll go for a run to burn off the calories. Then I'll go for another run just to make sure I did.

And what sort of person starts a tea and Tarot room? Not a temperate one, that's for sure. A temperate person wouldn't take that big of a risk. Or maybe they would, just... temperately.

But birth cards[1] aren't destiny. They're often the lesson you need to learn in this life. Or in my case, the lesson I'm resisting. I can usually manage detachment. But balance and patience? Ha! [2]

The Symbols

The Archangel of Temperance, representing the sublimation of earthly desires, has one foot in the watery world of spirit and emotion and one on the dry land of reason. We've been put on this earth for a reason, and it's not just to rise above the material. You don't have to choose one or the other. The answer is yes to *both*, but to pull this off requires balance.

The angel is neither male nor female. It pours water between two cups, symbolizing synthesis and combination. It has one foot in the water and one foot on land. The angel is balanced between the material earth and the emotional waters.

In the background, the path through the mountain gateway with the sun/crown rising above it reminds us of the path in the Death card. Death, of course, is about letting go and transformation. But you can't transform without Temperance's qualities of balance, detachment, and patience.

What Does This Card Mean for You?

---

1. Maybe explain birth cards here. They're calculated by adding the digits of your birth day, birth month, and then the first and last two digits of your birth year like so: DD + MM + YY + YY, and then adding the resulting numbers together to get the one or two digit number of your card. - T

2. Temperance is one of the Greek virtues, and to the Stoics it meant the self-discipline of moderation, of avoiding excess. It's about responding mindfully to situations rather than reacting. When someone does something to infuriate you, the Greek philosopher Seneca recommended applying temperance by asking ourselves if we've been guilty of the same? And how does getting angry do us any good?

   And I'm trying to be temperate, I'm really trying. But right now I'm having a harder time tempering my reactions. You don't know my family... - T

Life pulls us in so many directions at once, that it's easy to feel off balance. But with patience, integration—of opposing beliefs, positions, and people—is possible.

How can you bring more balance into your life?

THE DEVIL

SHADOW SIDE. ADDICTION. OBSESSION. *Illusion.*

He stumbled into my office smelling of stale alcohol and cigarettes. My business partner, Abigail, peered anxiously through the door behind him, her eyes wide. "Ah, I couldn't stop him, he—"

"I want a Tarot reading," he slurred, scratching his belly beneath his Hawaiian shirt.

"It's fine," I told her, and she nodded and retreated. Not every client who walks through my door is looking for self-reflection and inner growth. Some want a fun experience. Some just want to be told everything will be okay. Others...

Others arrived in California hot off stealing an alligator from a Florida golf course and trying to "teach it a lesson" by throwing it onto the thatched roof of a Tiki bar. The fact that my new client admitted this with a measure of pride told me our local greenways would soon be in for a treat.

"What was I supposed to do?" he asked. "That gator was following me everywhere. He ruined my game. It wasn't *my* fault. I didn't have any control over him. He *made* me do it."

I shuffled and drew a card. Color me unsurprised, it was the Devil.

My client waggled his unkempt brows. "I'm a lucky devil?"

"Not exactly."

The Symbols

In the card, a male and female figure are loosely bound to a rectangular, black stone. A devilish figure holding a torch perches on top. The man and woman are nearly identical to the two in the Lovers card. So it's no surprise that the number of the Devil card, fifteen, reduces to six numerologically (1 + 5), the same number as the Lovers. In the Garden, Adam and Eve were pure, and in the Lovers card we see an angel above them. But this shows us the same characters after the fall.

One major difference between these two Adam and Eve characters is the couple on this card have tails. Grapes hang from the end of the woman's tail, representing being bound to the material/earth plain. The man's tail is in flames, to show that he's ruled by his passions.[1]

This Tarot card can indicate a time you *feel* you have no control over the situation, when you're trapped and acting against your will. The man and woman here aren't tightly bound, though. Judging by the slack around their necks, they could easily slip those chains. But there's often a gap

---

1. There can be a sexual dimension to the Devil card, as well as in the Lovers. - T

between what one thinks and feels and what *is*, which is why this is also a card of illusion or willful blindness.[2]

Like the Florida Man's gator problem, the couple's problem here is entirely self-inflicted. And judging by the expressions on their faces, the man and woman in the card aren't entirely opposed to the situation.

What Does This Card Mean for You?

Sometimes we see what we want to see. And sometimes, for whatever reasons, we just can't get a full picture of the situation or even of our own

---

2. It's interesting that they call the Devil the Prince of Lies, when lying doesn't even rank among the seven deadly sins. One has to consider if he's so evil, why isn't he the prince of something like murder?

But what people have forgotten is that lies enable all the other sins. Lies prevent us from perceiving reality, whether they're the lies we tell ourselves, or lies we believe of others. The truth is everything, Hyperion. Everything. And there's no wiggle room for "your truth" or "my truth." Those are just pretty lies we tell ourselves. What matters is objective truth, no matter how difficult to reach or painful it may be to our egos. Because once we become enmeshed in lies, it's over. We're lost.   - T

motives. What illusions are keeping you locked in a negative pattern or situation?[3] [4]

---

3. Honestly? This is great, really it is. But I can't believe this is the story you're telling instead of the amazing encounter you had with the Devil that you emailed me all those years ago. I know you feel ashamed of it, but you need to include it somewhere. At the back of the book? As an addendum to this chapter? SOMEWHERE. - T

4. But enough about you. Since I brought up the Seven Deadlies, I feel compelled to tell you about a recent experience I had—a big dream.

   In the dream, I bent my knee to the Divine. It was all I could do, all I wanted to do, and I was filled with an ecstatic bliss that eroded the boundaries of my being. Around us were people engaged in the seven deadly sins. I wanted them to SEE. The Divine was here, right here. But they were too busy, too fixated on their petty sins. And then I woke up. I understood then that the Divine is always there, ready and reaching out to us, if only we can see it. But we blind ourselves to that energy when we don't follow the Way. - T

THE DEVIL ON A ROOFTOP

AUTHORS NOTE: I INCLUDED *this story at T's suggestion.*

You think you've heard weird?

I saw the Devil on a rooftop. No, not *that* Devil, not the Tarot card Devil of self-delusion and willful blindness and submitting yourself to what's not true. That's the devil inside us all. I'm talking about The Devil. Capital letters. Red skin. Naked and... Well, you wouldn't believe the size of his...

Stop looking at me that way.

You *know* what way. I was going to say the size of his *horns.*

Anyway, I was sixteen when he appeared leering beside the chimney. I laughed so hard at the full-tilt weirdness I choked on my stolen cigarette.

And no, hysteria's not what made me see the Devil. He was real. He was there, IRL. Besides, I read somewhere that laughter is a normal reaction when you see the Devil, so that just proves it was real. And how else was I *supposed* to react?

I definitely was *not* supposed to be on the roof avoiding my parents' dinner party. Or smoking. But, you know, they're scientists, so you can imagine how boring those parties were.

And... sixteen. Of course I'd escaped to the roof. Can you blame me?

Okay, that's not the point. The point is, I was close enough to reach out and touch him. I was so surprised by his appearance I nearly fell off the roof. But then he was gone, and I was choking and trying not to make too much noise because... Parents. Dinner party. Sixteen. Got it?

Plus, the Devil. You don't see *him* every day. I remember trying to slow my breathing, one hand pressing into a shingle so hard it left slivers in my palm. I remember looking around, trying to tell myself that there was a reality and I was in it, and there was the moon, and there the weak stars—there weren't many, too many city lights—and there was our detached garage where my father kept his makeshift lab with all its computers and chemicals.

And then Dr. Stapleton walked out of the house alone. My parents' colleagues insisted we use their titles, even though Stapleton was a doctor of physics and not a medical doctor. I found that more than a little precious then. I still do. *Titles.* Like we're in Regency England or something.

His wife was a doctor too. Astrophysics, I think. I liked her. She looked me in the eyes like I was a person and not a potentiality or a probability like my parents' other friends did.

She even tried to make conversation with me, poor woman. At sixteen, I was in my moody, tragic phase. I regret that now. Not being as friendly as I could have, I mean. The moody tragic teen phase was inevitable.

So Dr. Stapleton had escaped the party too. I smiled at that.

But then he speed walked to the garage, and something made the hair go up on the back of my neck. There was no reason for him to *not* walk to the garage or not to hurry. It was a cold night. But there was something… furtive in the way Stapleton moved.

He stopped beside the door and stared at the lit windows below me. And then he nodded to himself and walked inside. About ten minutes later, he walked out, looked around, and returned to the party.

That should have been it, but it bugged me. I didn't say anything to my parents though. Smoking. Roof. Dinner party. Sixteen. But it bugged me.

I should have said something.

A week later, the other Dr. Stapleton, the wife, was dead. Poisoned. The police arrested him of course. He'd been cheating on her. And like an idiot, he'd left fingerprints all over my father's garage. The doctor might have been a genius at physics, but he was useless at getting away with mu rder.

No, I *know* I was only sixteen. I'm not seeking absolution. I'm only trying to explain. If I had said something, she might have lived. Because deep down, even then, I *knew*.

I played a part in her death.

And I've always wondered...

No, *not* if that's why I do what I do.

Okay, maybe a little.

But I wonder, well, was the Devil a warning about him? Or was it about me?

THE TOWER

SUDDEN CHANGE. DESTRUCTION. UPSET.

It was one of those rare, spring lightning storms in San Borromeo. The flashes over the stormy gray Pacific were spectacular, but so were the torrents of water flooding my patio and seeping into my living room.

I should have stocked up on sandbags, but I hadn't. Fortunately, a friend brought some over, and that problem was solved... until my washing machine broke. Good thing the only person living below my laundry room is me. Only *my* walls were caving in from water damage. Yay, me.

Which brings me like a bad dream to the Tower card, which can indicate everything from a broken washing machine to something more dire.

Here's the thing. If you aren't willing to change, if you're stuck in your old ways and those ways aren't working, the universe will come along and give you a swift kick in the pants. That's the Tower. It turns everything upside down.

And if your washing machine has been making strange wheezy grindy sounds for the last month and you haven't taken any action to fix it... Much like the Tower card, the outcome is sort of inevitable.

The Symbols

In this card, two crowned figures plummet from a lightning-struck tower against a dark and stormy background. At the impact, a giant crown flies off the top of the tower.

Lightning can represent illumination, punishment, and reality. The ominous black background mirrors the black background in the Devil card. The tower itself is frequently referred to by Tarotistas as the Tower of Babel, which represented the ego of man (and which God destroyed). As such, the Tower represents one's ego, beliefs, and protective devices getting knocked flat. Sudden, dramatic, and painful change is on its way—unless *you* make a change first.

(While most Tarot readers see the Major Arcana as a natural progression of internal growth, I see it more as a choose-your-own-adventure. You can take the road of Death, let go, and move on to the virtue of Temperance. Or you can get lost in the illusion of the Devil, and head for the crash of the Tower.)

It's ultimately less painful to accept the death of the old and the birth of the new, rather than to fight it. So we may as well let go, get a move on, and fix that washing machine before it breaks down and the next thing you know, water is spewing all over your converted closet space. Especially since your condo association is quite clear that damage to the interior of the condo is your problem, not theirs.[1]

What Does This Card Mean for You?

The next time you see the Tower card, don't panic, but do get on all those niggling things you know you need to take care of. This includes dealing with bad habits and anything or anyone that is generally unhealthy for you. As in all Tarot readings, think of the cards' warnings as signposts to follow, and *not* promises of impending doom or delight.

---

1. My father died last night.

THE STAR

HOPE.[1] OPTIMISM. RENEWAL. TRANSCENDENCE. *Tranquility.*

Last week I got a phone call. "Fred's in hospice. He's asked to see you."

Fred was an elderly friend of my parents. I'd known him since I was a kid. As I got older, we stayed in touch, going out for lunch once every couple months. He was a bit like the grandfather I'd wished I'd had. Wise. Kindly. Funny.

It was a stormy spring night, and I raced through sheeting rain to the hospice at the top of a multistory, impersonal VA hospital. By the time I'd arrived, Fred was unresponsive.

In his room, the barren walls were broken only by twists of black cables for non-existent machines. I wondered how long he'd been staring at those awful blank walls before fading into unconsciousness.

---

1. Hope saved me. I've learned that cynicism—hope's true opposite—isn't just a cop-out; it's used to control. My father used it on us growing up. If we had no hope, there was no point in fighting him. I escaped by running. Charles and Adelaide gave up. Bad things still happened, but I survived because of hope. - T

His son had been there all day and needed a break, so he left and I sat by Fred's bed. His breathing changed, growing raspy. I hurriedly got his son from the cafeteria, and we returned to the room.

Fred and his son had had a fraught relationship. It's their story to tell, so I won't elaborate here. But the son was clearly at a loss and didn't know what to do. I told him to say his goodbyes, that Fred could still hear him. I didn't know this, but I believed it. I took one of Fred's hands and his son took the other, and we told him he was loved.

His son said goodbye, and Fred passed away. (And I know some people get grouchy about euphemisms for "died," but I really do think he went somewhere else, so the expression seems apt).

We cried. I went home.

The next day I was filled with a blissful joy I've only encountered once before. I can't explain it. I certainly wasn't *happy* Fred was gone. But I couldn't and didn't want to shake the pure light that filled my heart.

Was that feeling Fred, letting me know he was well? Was it something else? Whatever it was, everything felt *right* and good. The feeling stuck with me until I fell asleep that night, and the next morning I was back to "normal." But I won't forget that feeling.[2]

The Symbols

Whatever caused it, that experience was a deep Star moment. In Tarot's Major Arcana, The Star follows the destruction and disaster of the Tower card for good reason. Out of disaster can come renewal.

---

2. Because stars represent guides, in several traditions, the Star card also represents the psychopomp who guides souls from one world to the next. The seven smaller stars represent the Neoplatonic ladder of planets and ascension to the eighth sphere (the largest star). This is a card of spiritual ascension.

   It sounds as if you played the role of psychopomp that stormy night. You crossed the boundary and felt the oneness of the universe. For a time, you embodied the Star. Little wonder the power of it lingered on you. - T

The Star reminds us that there's something beyond, something bigger and better, and all we have to do is trust in it. The woman in the card is naked, representing purity—the ego is dissolved and laid bare. She pours water, suggesting a spiritual cleansing.

And notice that the woman's foot is on top of the water, not in it? We know this Tarot artist can draw feet *in* water, because she's done so in the Temperance card. So we can assume Pamela Colman Smith wasn't being sloppy here. She *meant* that foot to be on top of the water, as if the figure has transcended the mundane emotional world for something higher.

What Does This Card Mean for You?

When this card appears in a reading, consider if you're ready to take positive action and turn your dreams into reality, because now is the time for optimism. If you've recently been through a difficult time, meditate on how it may have affected your view on life. Take this time to release your worries, relax and recharge.

It will be okay.

THE MOON

MESSAGES FROM THE UNCONSCIOUS. *Mystery. Confusion. Dreams. Illusion.*

Last night, I dreamt of a departed aunt I'd had a contentious relationship with. She walked down the hallway of my apartment and sat beside me in the living room.

Suddenly I remembered she was dead and understood I was dreaming. But instead of the dream ending, like it usually does when I become aware, we talked—the kind of talk we'd never been able to have when she was alive. She apologized for some things she'd said and done and helped me understand why she'd said and done them. And her reasons weren't awful. They made a lot of sense.

I apologized too, because I hadn't been innocent in the turn our relationship had taken. We forgave each other. I woke up feeling lighter. Free.

The Symbols

I'm still not sure if it was "only" a lucid dream or a visitation from my relative. I don't know if it matters. It was all very lunar, very moonlike. And not just because the Moon card can represent dreams. Moons with their waxing and waning also represents illusion and confusion, messages from the subconscious crawling up out of the muck like that lobster creeping from the water in the card. A dog and a wolf, representing the refined conscious and the more primitive subconscious, howl at the moon's light.

And *all* of those things had been at play in my life. I'd created a false—or at least incomplete—story in my mind of the cause of my estrangement from my relative (illusion/confusion). But the truth bubbled up from my subconscious in last night's dream. If it hadn't, I'd still be carrying that burden.

What Does This Card Mean for You?

When the Moon card appears in a Tarot reading, it suggests we may not be seeing things clearly. But the truth is out there — or *in* there, as the case may be.

How can you bring your subconscious impulses or knowledge into conscious light? The road between the two towers in the card is long, dark, and winding. Have patience. Be brave.[1]

---

1. As to The Moon, I feel like I'm swimming in it. At first my father's death seemed like an accident, a fall from the balcony outside his bedroom. He's been drinking more than usual lately. But the servants swear he wasn't drinking that night. And the balcony railing is low. Could he have fallen by accident?

   I keep replaying our last conversation. Had he been thinking then of taking his own life? Was that why he'd come to see me? Because he knew I'd been a failure when I'd tried my hand at self-deletion? Maybe he wanted me to talk him out of it?

   I don't understand. But I'll try to keep up with the daily edits, where I feel I have something to add. I need to keep my mind busy. - T

The Sun

Enlightenment. Positivity. Warmth. Self-confidence. *Freedom. Conscious action.*

Her name was Kim, and she was a Georgia peach, sunny and tan and blonde. And when she walked into the hall, everyone gravitated toward her. She wasn't particularly beautiful. She was particularly ordinary—all except her heart, which was spilling over with love. It made her irresistible.

She'd come to my booth at the psychic fair when I was in despair about psychic fairs in general and this psychic fair specifically. Before I knew it, not only had I given her a reading, but somehow I'd given *myself* a reading, and she was cheering me out of *my* story of woe.

Her good nature was contagious. Now instead of counting the minutes until I could flee the fair, I was having a blast, the life of the party again.

We all know these people. They have a certain warmth, a charisma, that draws others in and lifts them up. Magic seems to happen for them and around them.

This quality isn't something other people have. We *all* have this solar energy inside us. But too often we play small or hide our true natures out of fear of rejection. We create our own clouds, obscuring who we are in the hopes for greater acceptance. But of course that only drives people away.

The Symbols

In this card, a naked child, freewheeling and self-confident, rides a white horse, representing vitality. Four sunflowers turn their heads to face the child instead of the actual sun behind them. The child is the true sun in this card. He's being his authentic self. He doesn't need clothing to present a certain image or to hide behind. The child has ventured outside the garden wall, choosing the risk of authentic experience over cloistered safety.

What Does This Card Mean for You?

Consider how the energies of this card—enlightenment, positivity, self-confidence, warmth, and freedom—may be working in your life, or where you need to bring more of them into your life. Are you secure enough to be fully, vitally present and to encourage others to shine?[1]

---

1. Or just lighten up and have some fun. - T

JUDGMENT

TRANSFORMATION. ANSWERING THE CALL. *Rebirth. Discernment.*

In storytelling, there's something called a "rebirth" plot type. Here's how it goes. Tell me if it sounds familiar.

Point 1: An evil presence, reeking of a bad dream, spreads its wings above our brave hero (let's just say, me, facing a marketing budget that's not big enough).

Point 2: Our brave hero chugs along, and seems to be doing okay, despite the fact he may have gone a *teensy* bit over budget.

Point 3: The shadow pounces, oppressing our hero to the point of despair. The extra cash I *thought* was coming in to cover the shortfall doesn't come in.

Point 4: Things get worse. There's an emergency at the tearoom, and that extra money I spent now needs to go elsewhere. I have to confess my sins. And figure this mess out.

Point 5: Huzzah! The hero confesses, breaks free, and is reborn. He comes into his power, learns his lessons, and life is better.

Actually, I'm still waiting to get to step five. I haven't told my partner about my spending gaffe... yet.

THE MYSTERIES OF TAROT

But I will, and I've got hope. It's spring as I write this, that liminal, in-between time when the earth is busting at its seams. Also, there's more sun, which I find energizing—so much so, that I'm making a point to spend more time outside soaking up vitamin D.

And that's kind of the point. Because unlike the spring flowers which burst effortlessly into bloom, we've got to take *steps*. The hero in our story doesn't suddenly, magically *become* free. He *breaks* free. There's no transformation without action.

And yes, I know transformation may seem exhausting. But wouldn't you rather be transformed, reborn, than stuck in the underworld?

On second thought, that sounds like my Saturday night.

The Symbols

The angel Gabriel awakens the dead with a trumpet blast, and they rise from their graves. A St. George's banner, representing innocence, hangs from the trumpet. This is an image of resurrection and rebirth, and the resurrected raise their arms in awe and joy.[1]

This is the endpoint of a successful transformation. The caskets are floating on water, a symbol of the emotional life, hinting that the transformation may be an emotional one. The land has been flooded, causing the coffins to loosen from the earth and bob to the surface, where the people inside them are called to a higher state.

Judgment is ruled by Pluto, god of the underworld, and is also associated with his wife, Persephone, infamous eater of pomegranate seeds.

---

1. Remember, the Tarot came out of the Renaissance. For people during that period, the Last Judgment was, yes, about rebirth, but it was also about being judged. So if Abigail blasts you when she learns what you did, sorry buddy. You deserved it. The word is right on the card.

Judgment also calls us to be discerning and to use our judgment. The Neoplatonists were concerned with truth, with good and evil. They recognized that there were people without conscience who would take advantage, and getting taken advantage by them, allowing oneself to be pulled from the truth, would take you off the path. Discernment is a critical tool to staying on that path. So don't be naïve. - T

Every spring, she rises, reborn, from the underworld to enjoy the earth. (Every fall she descends, but that's a story for another day).

What Does This Card Mean for You?

Are you ready to be reborn? If not, what might be blocking your transformation?[2]

---

2. If only it were that easy. - T

THE WORLD.

THE WORLD

ACCOMPLISHMENT. COMPLETION. SELF-ACTUALIZATION. CONNECTION *with the Divine.*

So I met a guy in a bar. (No, this story *isn't* going the way you think.)

I met a guy in a bar, and he was obviously having a rough time. His wife had left him. His kids hated him. *And* he'd lost his job.

We ended up having one of those late-night, meaning-of-life discussions that only happens over quality tequila. And in the end, we realized that the meaning of life was right here, right now. This moment and every moment. The struggle. The joy. All of it. But we only really *felt* it when we were connecting with each other.

I never saw him after that night. But the memory of our conversation has stayed with me.

The World is the final card in the Major Arcana, and it can mean several things. Completion of something you've been working to manifest. Self-actualization. Connection with the Divine. Accomplishment.[1]

But the ultimate goal is achieving meaning. Finding it. Having it. Because when you've got meaning, everything else falls into place.

The problem is, even when we find meaning, it's easy to forget about it. Life goes on, and only now and again do you look up and remember how damn lucky you are just to be alive.

So while this card can mean that *eureka* moment when all is well within and without, it also reminds us to wake up and look around.

The Symbols

The dancing woman is the Neoplatonic *anima mundi*, the world soul, or fifth element, which permeates the other four elements and is the loving intelligence which animates all. She holds two batons identical to the baton the Magician holds. But the World is playing with them rather than using them to draw the energy of heaven down to earth, because she already *has* that magical power.

Her legs are crossed in a position similar to that of the Hanged Man, though she stands right-side up. The lesson of the Hanged Man has been learned and integrated. In the corners of the card are an eagle, lion, bull, and man.[2] I went into them in more detail in the Wheel of Fortune, if you want to check that out.

A surprising number of people come to a reading wanting to know their life's purpose. Usually what they really want to know is what type of job will make them happy. But deep down, we all have the same purpose—to live, to truly live. The woman in the World card has figured it out, dancing in the moment, surrounded by symbols of the four elements.

---

1. And this is why some people see the virtue of Prudence in this card. The World is the culmination of the Major Arcana and its virtues. And Prudence, which pairs right action (or words) with right timing is true wisdom and the culmination of the ancient Greek virtues. - T

2. The placement of these four creates what's called a quincunx, with four figures in the corner representing the physical world and a sacred image in the center. - T

What Does This Card Mean for You?

Life is pretty amazing. It's also short. So we should strive to experience meaning in every moment of every day. And if you're not, look at the people around you. There's your meaning. Right now.

What would it take for you to feel complete today?

THE SUIT OF PENTACLES

EARTH

Abundance

Foundations

Fertility

The physical world

Health and home[1]

---

1. I'm regrouping with a thorough cleaning of my temporary home. And yes, the caretaker's cottage was already clean, but I felt driven to... Start fresh now that my father's gone?

Adelaide stopped by, catching me in the middle of scrubbing behind the stove. She thought I was mad not to call in the servants. But that wasn't the point. The point was rolling up my sleeves and getting dirty. Laughing, she left me to it.

What finally stopped me was discovering an old plastic yellow house at the back of the closet. It was my mother's. When we were kids, she'd bring it out for Christmas and create a little village beneath the tree. An old mirror became an ice skating rink. Cotton for snow. This was before my father got big and mom got cancer. You know the rest.

I cried for the first time since his death, not just for the past but for what could have been. Could things have changed between us? It seemed like he was trying. Like something had changed.

Why, Hyperion? Why did he do it? -T

ACE OF PENTACLES

NEW OPPORTUNITIES. MANIFESTATION. ABUNDANCE. *Prosperity.*

A friend of mine, a struggling restauranteur, called to ask how best to deal with a disaster. Her car had been stolen while she'd been pumping gas. The police weren't being particularly helpful. They were pessimistic about the odds of her getting it back.

I drew the Ace of Pentacles and suggested there was an opportunity lurking in all those clouds. I didn't see what that opportunity might be. But I've learned to trust the cards.

What happened next stunned me. She'd been in the habit of misplacing her keys around the house, so she'd put a tracker on her keyring. She used it to track her keys *and* the car they were inside, stole back her car, informed the police, and got a date with a detective. The papers got wind of the story, published the name of her restaurant, and hungry guests flooded in.

Put a "results not typical" asterisk on that tale. And I'm *not* recommending anyone chase down car thieves on their own. The point is, in Tarot, aces can be explosive and startling and hand you a lot more than you expected.

As the first card in their suit, aces represent the start of things, possibilities. The ace holds all the potential of its suit and can channel the energies of any of its suit cards. In the case of pentacles, which represent the material plane—work, health, money, etc.—it could be a prod to start that healthy eating plan or a hint at a career opportunity.

But.

The Ace of Pentacles doesn't call for, you to laze on the couch waiting for that opportunity to come to you. It's up to you to seize the day, take the chance, go for it. Maybe not *quite* the way my friend did, but you get the picture. No guts, no glory. Ignore an opportunity, and it vanishes.

The Symbols

A hand extends from clouds and offers a golden coin. Beneath it is a garden's arbor entrance covered in lilies and roses. The arbor forms a doorway, representing a new beginning. Lilies represent vision and pure thoughts. Roses represent will and desire. A straight, smooth trail leads to the arbor; attainment comes easily if you take the path.

What Does This Card Mean for You?

What opportunities have you been ignoring? Now is the time to manifest. Get off the couch. Take action.[1]

---

1. And sometimes the Ace means prosperity just lands in your lap, whether you like it or not. Hyperion... The bulk of my father's estate... It's going to me. And I have no idea what to do with it. Split it with Adelaide and Charles, obviously. I don't know what my father was thinking by leaving them such small shares. As to the rest of the money, I don't know. I'd like to do something positive with it to make up for the lives he ruined. But I'm not sure that's possible. - T

TWO OF PENTACLES

BALANCE IN THE FACE *of turbulence. Juggling priorities. Challenging times.*

Where were you when... the Towers fell, the Challenger exploded, the Boston Bombing destroyed so many lives? Some friends and I were playing that game over tequila, and I realized that most of these "where were you when" days were awful.

Those events all sent us spinning—for a time at least. And in some instances, the reactionary societal changes that followed stuck with us, and not for the better.

The Symbols

There's a lot we can't control. Natural disasters, societal shifts, that surprise audit. All we can do is control our reactions. We can be the man in Tarot's Two of Pentacles, dancing on shifting sands in front of a storm-tossed sea. He's unable to affect or assist the ships floundering on the high waves. Like him, sometimes all we can realistically manage is our own little world, the pentacles in our hands.

In the card, the course of those two pentacles is traced by an infinity sign, reminding us that this juggling act requires constant effort. The world goes on, we're small pieces in it, and as long as we're alive, we need to dance with it.

When life strikes, good or bad, large or small, are we reacting? Or are we dancing, keeping our balls in the air, staying centered? To lose our center is to lose our balance, and then those pentacles will come crashing d own.

This Tarot card challenges us, asking where we are internally, so we can manage our reactions to external pressures. And it reminds us that when everything's going sideways, we need to keep the important pieces of our own worlds intact—whether that means keeping up an exercise regime, *not* burying our sorrows in food and drink, or just continuing to get up, get dressed, brush our teeth, and move on. On a more prosaic level, it asks us what balls we may be dropping that maybe shouldn't be dropped.

What Does This Card Mean for You?

The Two of Pentacles reminds us to stay centered and stay balanced. You may not be able to control the whirlwind around you, so focus on what you can manage. You can control *you*.[1]

What can you realistically control in this situation?

---

1. Thanks for the reminder. This is a very Stoic philosophy, but it takes practice to implement. I feel like that man on the shore now. There's so much to deal with after my father's death, and I'd rather fall back into my old habits and hide. But I won't. Not today. - T

THREE OF PENTACLES

WORK. TEAMWORK. LEARNING.

I have had some *rough* jobs. Trust me. My work was not all glamour and magical fun before Beanblossom's Tea and Tarot. I've worked retail (brutal). I've waited tables (even worse). But I can't help but thinking that doing those jobs *well* was what got me here, as part-owner of the best tea and Tarot room on the California coast. Because when I tried to do my best, I learned useful lessons from those jobs, and I made good connections.

You never know where work will take you or what you'll learn. What made my awful jobs livable was focusing on my values: doing the job right, being challenged, being of service.

What made me crazy was when other important values, like being in control of my earnings and having freedom to do things when and how I wanted *weren't* fulfilled. Those were the pain points that drove me to going it alone as a Tarot reader and, eventually, going in on a tearoom.

The Symbols

Threes represent expression, creation, fertilization, and growth, the first manifestation of something real and supportive. In this card we see a mason at work on creating something divine—a church. This isn't a ho-hum job. He can't just phone it in. He's building something important, and the details matter.

He consults with two others. He can't do it all on his own. This endeavor takes teamwork.

What Does This Card Mean for You?

If life is getting you down, this card asks what would happen if you thought of your activities as a calling instead of a grind. And if you're loving what you do, the Three of Pentacles is telling you to keep at it and look to possible collaborators or people to learn from.[1]

Who can you collaborate with?

---

1. I slunk into my father's house like a criminal, avoiding the staff, the stepmom, everyone, and climbed the marble stairs to my father's room. I'm not sure what I was looking for. A reason, maybe.

   The police aren't calling it a suicide. I doubt they ever will. No one wants to go on record that someone like my father would do this.

   I surprised one of the maids as I was leaving, but she was too startled to challenge me. Not that she really could. It's my house now. - T

FOUR OF PENTACLES

HOARDING. INVESTMENT. INSECURITY. HOLDING *on.*

Yesterday, on the advice of a techie friend, I bought my first hundred dollars of cryptocurrency. It's 2022 as I write this, so I'm well behind the crypto curve. What held me back was laziness and ignorance. I readily admit the purchase may blow up in my face.

The process was a major hassle, involving a crazy level of passwords, proof I am who I say I am, and a ridiculous amount of backing and forthing online. I'd been advised to buy a special offline "wallet," but I have to wait a week before I can deposit any of the crypto I bought into it. There's a high probability I'll forget to do so until my friend reminds me.

For me, buying the crypto was more a statement of financial anarchy than a means of exchange or even an investment. The subversive glow I feel from owning crypto was well worth the hundred bucks. And yes, that's a terrible reason to buy anything, but I'll probably buy more.

When it comes to spending and holding money, we have lots of terrible, unexamined reasons for our actions. We infuse money with all sorts of meaning. Security. Power. Freedom. Love. That's how it begins to control u s.

I like making money, but I tend not to hang onto it. It's a pattern, and we all have patterns around money. Some spend money as fast as they make it. Others have massive credit card debt. The Four of Pentacles asks us to examine these patterns, and how they might be manifesting in other areas of our lives.

The psychological aspects of money are huge. In some of us, the idea money is the root of all evil is embedded deep. In others, money's a measure not only of value, but of their personal self-worth.

Some diligent folks (like my business partner, Abigail), wisely save and invest. I told her I'd help set her up to buy crypto—for savings and investment purposes—and she threw a scone at me. I deserved it. (And it was an excellent scone).

Abigail's not the miser on the Four of Pentacles, but she does tend to hang on to people—maybe longer and harder than she should. Our relationship with money can be a metaphor for other relationships.

The Symbols

In this card, a Midas-like figure grips a pentacle between two hands, wears one as a crown, and traps a coin beneath each foot.[1] He wears a black cloak of fear and uncertainty, and he hunches protectively over his wealth. This is a card of clinging, of grasping.

What Does This Card Mean for You?

The Four of Pentacles asks us to consider what we're holding onto, and if it's time to invest or just let go. Let your inner voice and the other cards in the spread guide your answer.

What are you clinging to?

---

1. This card is my father, and all his clinging to his wealth and power kept him separate from the people that should have mattered—his family. When you're holding onto one thing, you can't embrace others. I'm glad the fire forced me from my hermit life in the forest now. Even though I didn't willingly release that life (I can be Four of Pentacles too), once I did, I got the chance to say goodbye to him, even though I didn't know it would BE a goodbye. - T

FIVE OF PENTACLES

POVERTY MINDSET. SENSE OF *lack. Sense of inadequacy. Woe is me.*

Thirty percent of restaurants fail in their first year. It wasn't a statistic I gave much thought to when we started up Beanblossom's Tea and Tarot.

I couldn't stop thinking about it after the tearoom opened. I didn't talk about my worries though. My partner was stressed enough for the both of us. But that statistic had wormed its way inside my brain, and it wasn't helping my vibe.

I don't pretend to know the woo-woo behind it all, or even if there *is* woo-woo behind mindset and manifestation. But it definitely seems that when you're in a positive frame of mind, positive things happen. Maybe your mind is more open to possibilities and opportunities. Maybe people just want to be around happy people, and as a species we've succeeded mainly through our ability to cooperate with each other.

Whatever. A positive mindset *works.*

Anyway, during that period, the Five of Pentacles kept turning up in my daily draws. It got irritating, because yeah, I *knew* what it meant. I was not doing myself any favors by focusing on the budgets and everything that went wrong in our operations. And trust me, plenty went wrong that first year.

The Symbols

In the Five of Pentacles, two ragged figures trudge through the snow, past a stained-glass church window. One is on crutches, just to hammer home how pathetic their situation is.

But though this card looks dire, I've always seen it as a card of hope. A stained-glass window represents movement of mind, body, and spirit. Snow can represent the opposite—a lack of progress or momentum. Forward movement is possible if the two figures get out of the snow and go inside. But will they notice the shelter, or are they too fixated on their current path to see it?

There's also a "woe is me" aspect to the card. The scene is a *bit* high drama. So it could represent a time in our lives when we're playing the "poor me" card.

What Does This Card Mean for You?

It's easy to fall into a mentality of lack. But it can be turned around. How much is your mindset affecting the situation?[1]

---

1. Not well, Hyperion. Not well at all. - T

Six of Pentacles

Generosity. Contribution. Giving and *Receiving*.

Is it *really* better to give than to receive?

Now there's nothing wrong with receiving. I *adore* getting presents.

But giving, contributing, being generous, is one of the best things we can do for our souls. You know it's true, because you know how *good* it feels.

There are many ways to give. I'm not just talking about donating money or charitable giving. We can give time to mow an elderly neighbor's lawn. We can give attention to a child. We can give our skills and knowledge. There's a whole host of contributions we can make.

But where to start? The world's problems can feel overwhelming. It's why I've been avoiding social media like the plague of crazy that it is. After a session of doomscrolling, all I want to do is move to a deserted island. (Know any? Preferably with all the amenities).

But here's what's *really* crazy. The more we stress and rage about the rotten things other people are doing, the less we actually do good or are good for the people closest to us. Anger and outrage are a contagion. And when they're paired with cynical resignation, things get worse.

Here's the secret though. You can change the world if you start with yourself.

Illuminate your own little corner of the planet. Each flame in the darkness inspires others. The small things add up. The smiles, the kindnesses—they're contagious too.

The Symbols

In the Six of Pentacles, a man dispenses charity to two kneeling mendicants.[1] This card asks us first which character we play in the card—the giver or the receiver? And then it asks us to explore that character's positive and negative qualities and how they might apply to our life.

What Does This Card Mean for You?

If the giver is speaking to you, the card asks how you can expand this giving quality in your life. Is the giver acting selflessly or going for social credit points? And if it's the receiver you relate to, is the receiver grateful or needy?

What action can you take to light up your soul today?

---

1. And once again, life imitates art, art being your manuscript. My sister Adelaide dropped by my cottage today. She found Oswald charming, and we hugged and agreed how awful the situation was. But it didn't take a genius to figure out why she was here. She wanted to know my plans for the money. I told her I intended to split it between us three. Greed soon overrode her relief, and she switched to pitching her animal rescue, since obviously I didn't need SO much money. It couldn't have been more Six of Pentacles if she'd gotten on her knees and begged. Tarot can be terrifyingly direct.

   I told Adelaide I'd think about it. She didn't go away happy.

   But "charity" isn't only about money. It's also about kindness and consideration. To be charitable also means to be forgiving and nonjudgmental. Adelaide means well. For the first time, I was in the power position in my family. I don't like how it felt. There can be an ugly side to giving. I don't think she understands that. - T

Seven of Pentacles

An investment coming to fruition. Harvest. Overwhelm. Hard work leading to rewards.

My business partner and I had been working our tails off at Beanblossom's Tea and Tarot. The good news was all that hard work seemed to be paying off. We'd had a great holiday season. We *have* a terrific location. And the word was getting around about our tearoom.

We weren't rolling in ducats. I'm not sure if we ever will. But we had a livelihood and were helping others make a living, and the work was fun and rewarding.

It was also exhausting. And while I included blowing-off-steam in my daily to-do's... Heh, who am I kidding? I've *never* had a to-do list. The point is, I was handling it.

My partner Abigail... not so much. If she didn't take a vacation and soon, she was going to blow.

The Symbols

In the card, we see a man leaning on his hoe and studying seven pentacles growing from a lush bush. His mouth is downturned, his head is slumped. The pentacles are ready to harvest, but he looks tired. He's worked hard for this harvest, and he's earned this win.

What Does This Card Mean for You?

While all Tarot cards have multiple meanings, the Seven of Pentacles is particularly cattywampus. What this card means for you depends on the timing.

If you draw this card and you're at the beginning of a project, it's a reminder that putting in the work may not be easy, but it will be worth it. If you're nearing the end of the endeavor, it's a "don't give up now" card, because good things are coming. But depending on the cards surrounding it, it can also be a reminder to step back, realize how far you've come, and enjoy your progress.[1]

What would happen if you stopped to take stock?

---

1. I don't think I'm near the end of this hell. It feels like things are just beginning. - T

EIGHT OF PENTACLES

DEVELOPING SKILLS. MASTERY. WORK. *Craftsmanship.*

Did I mention love and money were two of the biggest reasons people came in for readings? Well, put love at the top of the list.

Margaret was a successful financial advisor. She wasn't too busy for love. But she'd never managed to make it happen, and the day she walked in my door she was feeling the lack.

"One card. That's all I need." A grin flitted across her puckish face. "I'm frugal."

I drew the Eight of Pentacles. "Hm."

She leaned across the round table for a better view. "*Hm* I'm doomed? Or *hm* there's an amazing man in my future?"

"Hm. You need to get focused and get to work."

"Ah... How? Because trust me, I've been trying to make this happen."

"Regularly?"

"Well, no," she admitted. "I mean, I guess I go in spurts. I sign up for a dating website and then get discouraged. And then later maybe I'll try again when I feel like it."

I shook my head. "When you became a financial advisor, did you just work at it when you felt like it?"

Margaret laughed. "Are you kidding? I worked at it every day."

I tapped the card. "You need to do the same here. Steady, consistent effort, every day."

Her shoulders hunched. "Every day? Who has the time?"

"What about ten minutes a day focused on making love happen? Not just working on finding guys online, but on becoming a better partner yourself. Put it in your calendar. Over time, the steady work will pay off."

She gave me a thoughtful look. "That... actually makes sense."

The Eight of Pentacles can be a reminder to keep plugging away at a skill. It can also hint that it's time to polish up an old skill (that fallen coin beneath the bench) or to learn a new one.

Real mastery takes repeated, conscious effort. My old martial arts instructor told us we'd need to practice a move ten-*thousand* times before we'd really know it. So if this card appears, don't give up. Look on this card as an opportunity for betterment, and a promise that with the work, comes a reward.

Twelve months later a photo pinged into my texts. A picture of Margaret's hand wearing an engagement ring.

The Symbols

The Eight of Pentacles is all about skills — their development and their mastery. This card depicts a craftsman hammering away at a golden coin. Seven identical coins have already been completed. Six hang from a nearby post. A seventh lies beneath his workbench. He's been working a long time on the same, repetitive activity, mastering his craft.

What Does This Card Mean for You?

Wouldn't it be boring if we had nothing to learn? What can you work on today?[1]

---

1. The Stoics believed continually working on yourself was one of the keys to a happy and well-lived life.

Joan stopped by to "see how I was managing." It's hard to describe my stepmother, but she makes an interesting study for the Eight of Pentacles. The negative side of eights can represent oppression and being overly emotional. She was certainly emotional and playing up the "I'm oppressed" card today, rolling up with her black-suited driver in her black limo and wearing a little black dress. Highly skilled craftsman? Check. She sure worked my father. Which is why I'm surprised he left her so little in the will. She'll get a small stipend now that he's gone and can remain in the house that belongs to me, but that's all. I'm surprised to find I feel genuinely sorry for her. She can't see beyond the material. The Eight of Pentacles is about seeing a project through to the end though, and I have a feeling Joan's play for my sympathy is only the beginning. - T

NINE OF PENTACLES

ABUNDANCE. DOMINION. SELF-SUFFICIENCY. ATTAINMENT.

It had been a wet spring, and I was road tripping with a friend from Denver to Huntington Beach. Chains were required going over the Rockies. But the roads were fairly clear and I didn't *have* chains, so we chugged up the mountain anyway, trucks throwing muddy snow onto my windshield. The windshield wiper froze somewhere near the summit. We had to keep pulling over to clean the window so I wouldn't drive off the road.

But we made it down the Rockies, whizzing through spectacular red rock canyons and into a desert in full bloom. I'd never seen it so green, and the contrast of wildflowers and red earth was spectacular.

Then finally... California. It was night by this time, and the mother of all storms struck. Lightning knifed into the desert around us.

I edged my nose closer to the windshield, as if the extra six inches would improve my vision through the blurring rain. Big rigs pulled off the freeway, not wanting to risk it. We kept going.

By the time we reached our beach house we were wired, but in a good way. Two death-defying experiences plus the spectacle of I-70 in the spring had blasted our senses with wonder and euphoria. We were in an amazingly luxurious beach house. (Don't ask how—I still can't explain it on our budget). The feeling that not only could we attain anything, but we were in a truly magical place in our lives, lasted the entire week. We'd *worked* to get to that beach house, and the payoff was amazing.

The Symbols

Which brings us to the woman in her garden in the Nine of Pentacles. As the last single digit in the series, nine is the number of completion and attainment.

And though I rarely talk about astrological aspects of cards, I'm going to break my rule and do it here, because I think it's important. The Nine of Pentacles is associated with Venus and Virgo. Venus is the planet of luxury. Virgo represents (among other things), being grounded and hard work. Put those two together, and you get well-earned luxury that remains emotionally grounded.

You can see those elements in the symbols of the card. The garden, the woman's fine clothing, and the grapes represent luxury. The castle in the background symbolizes security and self-determination. The snail in the foreground is also self-contained, carrying its home on its back. The falcon represents wisdom, determination, and self-discipline. And the mountains in the background represent attainment, realization of aspirations.

It's all there if you look. The woman in this card isn't just enjoying her luxurious garden. She's *earned* that enjoyment, and that makes it all the sweeter.

What Does This Card Mean for You?

If this card appears in a reading, it's a sign of good things to come—the completion of a project, or a sense of coming enjoyment and ease. But depending on its position and the cards around it, the Nine of Pentacles can also bring up some important life issues.

Are you taking the time to enjoy your accomplishments?[1]

---

1. Something's... not right. I had another spectacular vision. The woods around my house became a lush garden. I could see the life and vitality of every berry and leaf, every tree and stone. The world was pulsing with fertility and abundance, and I was part of it. But I lost time. Lots of it. And I felt like hell afterward. It took me a day to recover. - T

TEN OF PENTACLES

FAMILY. FINANCIAL ABUNDANCE. CONTRIBUTION. *Gratitude.*

As I write this, my gut is still busting from Thanksgiving with the family. Guilt is pointless. I know I'll do it again next year, because that's what my family *does*. We cook, we eat, we toast our good fortune. And even during the darkest days, there's plenty of good fortune to be found. There's all that food and family for starters.

The Symbols

The Ten of Pentacles is Thanksgiving. On the card, a happy family gathers to celebrate the good things in their lives. This is the card of home and hearth. It reminds us to count our blessings. In the future position in a reading, it promises good things to come.

The multiple generations in the card reminds us that wealth of all kinds—emotional, physical, spiritual, and financial—is built over time and through our long-term relationships with others. But like anything else, it takes effort.

What Does This Card Mean for You?

It's a funny thing, but when we focus on the abundance currently in our lives, more seems to magically come our way. How can you bring the

Thanksgiving spirit of family, goodwill, and gratitude into your life today (minus the overindulgence)?[1]

---

1. Don't forget that the pentacles on the RWS card are arranged in a Tree of Life design from the Kabbalah. Malkuth (Kingdom/Reality), is the tenth point on the Tree and represents the world of manifestation. This makes the 10 of Pentacles a manifestation card as well. - T

PAGE of PENTACLES

Page of Pentacles

STUDY. LEARNING NEW SKILLS. *Beginner's mind. A message or opportunity.*

A lot of really good martial artists are a little nuts. These are people who've dedicated their lives to learning how to take people *apart*. It's not that they're necessarily lovers of violence, but it takes a certain sort of person to devote that many hours to the practice. (FYI, I'm only a middling martial artist.)

In class last week, the sensei went on a rant about people who "know" things. "You don't know the move," he shouted. "You say, *uh-huh, got it*, but you *don't* got it. You have to practice a move ten thousand times." And on and on and on. It was a familiar rant, and thankfully not directed at m e.

But as I glanced at the others in the class, I realized the really good students were the ones who were focused on the details. They assumed they *didn't* know the move and kept digging deeper and deeper. They kept their beginner's mind. They kept learning where others just slopped through the moves and stagnated. And they practiced. A *lot*.

The Symbols

The Page of Pentacles card shows a young man studying a golden coin.

So who exactly *is* this page? He's a young man, and that speaks to a certain level of either immaturity or innocence. He's a student. He stands in a blooming meadow beneath a clear sky, representing promising beginnings and clear thought.

All the Pages correspond to the earth element. Since Pentacles is an earth suit, this is basically a double-earth card. Make of that what you will.

What Does This Card Mean for You?

If this card pops up in a reading and reminds you of someone, that's a good sign to spend some time thinking about how that someone is affecting your situation or how they could assist it. If it doesn't seem like anyone in your circle, then the card is likely calling on you to bring the positive elements of this Page into the situation. Alternately, you could examine where the negative elements of the Page might be hurting the situation.

How might approaching the issue with a beginner's mind illuminate the situation?[1]

---

1. Do I need to look at this situation with beginner's mind? There's a Russian word I love, ostranenie. It means to look at the familiar as if it's new, strange, and unfamiliar. I've gotten so used to the story in my head about my family. Brutal father, selfish siblings, gold-digging stepmother. But is it true? Do I need to look at my family with fresh eyes? - T

KNIGHT OF PENTACLES

PATIENCE. STEADINESS. DETERMINATION. PRACTICAL *action.*

"Can we start *now*?" I asked my burly contractor friend.

He grunted. "No."

I sighed and shifted my weight. All I wanted was a new ceiling for my office. We weren't even removing the old ceiling—just covering over the pipes that made my reading room look like an industrial basement.

But my friend had spent most of the morning measuring, taking notes, returning to the home supply store for more supplies, and *not* starting on the actual ceiling. Since he's the one with the contractor's license, I bit back my impatience, stole a scone from the tearoom kitchen, and waited.

When we finished (and I'll be honest; he did most of the work), the ceiling was perfect. And we got it all done that day. So in the end, his seeming slowness actually ended up going pretty fast.

I was grateful and humbled, and I rewarded him with more stolen scones from the tearoom kitchen. And of course I paid him too. But that's not the point. The point is, his stubborn, Knight of Pentacles energy was powerful stuff.

The Symbols

The Knight sits upon a steed at a standstill, a pentacle in his hand. He's planted. Steady. He's not charging around like the other knights. But even though he's not moving, he's still a knight, and knights get it *done*. The Knight of Pentacles just takes his time, sizing up all the angles, slow, and steady, and seeking the most practical approach.

The details in this card are also telling. The plowed field is a symbol of earth. It also represents a work in progress, the road ahead, and the promise of harvest.

Oak leaves adorn the Knight's helmet and horse. Oak leaves were sacred to thunder-and-lightening gods like Zeus and Thor. They're also connected to the Oak King and Green Man, both of whom cannot be killed. In Rome, oak leaves were a sign of service to the state, representing endurance and strength. Bottom line? The oak symbolizes an unstoppable force. So does this knight.

What Does This Card Mean for You?

Since Court Cards represent personality traits that may bear on the situation, it's useful to think of the positive *and* negative side of this knight. Determination can turn to stubbornness. Cautiousness can be taken too far. The hardworking knight can become dull.[1]

How are this knight's energies bearing on the situation at hand?

---

1. My brother stopped by. In his typical, plodding way, Charles ignored all my hints for him to go and made us mugs of tea. The tea was just what I needed, though I'm ashamed to say I did not tell him that. Especially since he was obviously feeling me out about my inheritance. (I can't believe Adelaide didn't tell him my plans). I was so out of sorts, for a fleeting moment I considered pretending I was keeping it all. But my better nature won out. I admitted I intended to split it so that we all walked away with equal portions of the estate.

Charles wasn't as relieved as I'd expected. But he's always been a strange bird. He's great at solving problems, but when he's not busy enough, he becomes self-critical and critical of others. And he's a real perfectionist—

Oh, damn. He's the Knight of Pentacles reversed. What's going on? Am I seeing the connections because I'm working on your manuscript, or are they really there? Is the universe playing a colossal joke on me? - T

QUEEN _of_ PENTACLES

Queen of Pentacles

Nurturing. Practical. Mothering.

As a newbie Tarotista, I had a mentor named June. Her graying hair was cut in a severe style, and as an ex-cop she was a no-B.S. style Tarot reader. June wasn't famous. She never really put herself out there. But she was in high demand and by people in surprisingly high places.

One day, when she'd come to observe me reading at a Psychic Fair, June pulled me aside. "You can't talk to your clients like that," she said.

Fair attendees wandered past us in the echoing hall. Distracted, I wondered how many readings this little sidebar was costing me. "Like what?" I asked, glancing at potential clients.

"You can't just tell someone their relationship is, and I quote, 'a dumpster fire in a fireworks factory.'"

I folded my arms. Who was June to cramp my style? "I was telling her what I saw in the cards. And I told her the relationship was salvageable. I even told her _how_ to salvage it." I'd given that client damned good advice, and I was proud of it. I'd been _helping_.

June sighed and cocked her head, a slight smile playing about her lips. "Did I ever tell you about the time I walked up on five grown men looting an electronics store?"

"Uh, no." I'd definitely have remembered that.

"It was in SF. There was a riot. I shouldn't have been on my own, but I'd gotten separated, and..." She shrugged. "...long story. The point is, I walked around the corner in my uniform, and there they were, pulling stereo parts out of a broken window."

"What'd you do?"

"I put on my best mommy voice, and said, 'Now boys, you know you're not supposed to be taking that. Put it back and go home.' They hung their heads, returned the stuff, and shuffled off."

"And this has to do with my dumpster fire comment, how?" I asked, interested despite myself.

"Sometimes you can lay things on the line. You can be the dad. But sometimes, you've got to be the mom. When you told your client her relationship was a dumpster fire, she shut down. She didn't hear what you told her next. She was too in shock. I'm not telling you to lie about what you see. I'm telling you to work your way through the cards so the client sees it herself. Lead her to her own conclusion, and then she'll be open to hearing about possible next steps. I'm telling you to be more nu rturing."

June pulled a card from the top of her deck. Flipping it over, she set it on my table. "I'm telling you to be the Queen of Pentacles. In charge, practical, but kind."

Now, my mentor had *totally* stacked her deck to draw the Queen. But she was also right.

It was super irritating.

But when the fair ended that night, I started a deep dive into that card to figure out the Queen's energies and how to bring them into my readings. Here are some of the things I noticed.

The Symbols

The Queen of Pentacles cradles the Pentacle in her lap as if it were a child. She sits in her garden—something which must be nurtured and cared for—at home in her earth element.

A cherub and a rabbit are carved into her throne. A bird nests in her crown. Combine all this fertility and motherhood symbolism with the mature feminine qualities of the queens, and you get a mothering and nurturing personality, especially since Pentacles can symbolize home and hearth, as well as work and money.

It took me some time to figure out how to draw these nurturing but practical qualities into my Tarot readings. Asking the right questions, I've found, can be a good way to help clients see things for themselves.[1]

What Does This Card Mean for You?

Where does the Queen of Pentacles need to be brought into your current situation? Or how is she operating there now?

---

1. The card can also mean the client's pregnant. There's not always an esoteric meaning. - T

KING OF PENTACLES

DISCIPLINE. RELIABILITY. LEADERSHIP. ABUNDANCE.

Every now and again my friend Riga's husband will sneak in for a reading. I say "sneak," because his appearance is always casual, accompanied by a nod and a this-is-just-for-fun wink. He's got a King of Pentacles personality, so taking a Tarot reading seriously isn't in his wheelhouse.

But I don't mind, because here's what *is* in his wheelhouse. He's a wealthy entrepreneur who has helped a lot of people with his personal and professional philanthropy. He's a man of discipline and abundance. If he says he'll do something, you can count on it.

Because he consistently works at the details of his life *every day*—whether that's in his relationships, his business, or his health—he excels at them all. He once mentioned he reads ten pages of Greek philosophy every morning. It may not seem like much, but over the course of years, he's become close to an expert. And while I don't have that sort of discipline, I admire it in others, especially when it garners such remarkable results.

The Symbols

Like all the Kings, the King of Pentacles is the master of his domain, and this suit is about the physical world and taking action in it. He wears a crown of roses and lilies, symbolizing (respectively) authority and the twin paths of passion and purity, devotion and knowledge. We see these roses and lilies in the Magician card as well, and this King is a lot like him in that he can manifest his desires through the magic of disciplined a ction.

His black cloak (the color of the earth element, like his throne) is decorated with grapevines, which are symbols of luxury, life, harvest, and the mysteries of the natural world. He's no austere Emperor figure. The King of Pentacles enjoys life and all it has to offer.

What Does This Card Mean for You?

Like the other Court Cards, he could represent you or someone around you. How are this king's energies operating in your life? Or do you need to bring some more King of Pentacles energy to the situation?[1]

---

1. I love this card. He feels like the Emperor and Empress combined — disciplined and abundant, reliable and compassionate.

My father was diligent but lacked the charity of this King. All his work was turned inward to the exclusion of the people around him.

I'm not bitter. I can't despise him, because I went through my own period of selfish introspection. I thought I was doing shadow work, but I did it without self-compassion and self-respect. I let my health fall apart, stopped working out, barely ate, and spiraled so deep I eventually checked myself into a mental institution. Not many people know that about me. It took me a long time to understand that self-love wasn't just compassion—it also required discipline. Compassion alone can too easily turn to permissiveness and weakness. Because when you respect yourself, you don't equate self-care or self-compassion with lying on the couch playing video games, eating pizza, and indulging in self-pity. Like I did. - T

THE SUIT OF SWORDS

AIR

Thoughts

Communications

Intellect

Rationality

ACE OF SWORDS

New ideas. Breakthrough. Triumph. *Revelation. Clarity. Opportunity.*

"Is it possible," I asked over coffee, "that a part of you *wants* to hold onto the pain?"

Gayle nearly spat out her cold brew. "Are you out of your ever-loving mind?"

She was a forty-something exec from a Silicon Valley company That Shall Not Be Named. Though she was killing it in the boardroom, her romantic life was a shambles.

"I just can't move on," she'd told me as we'd picked up our coffee. "Why can't I move on? I only dated this guy three weeks. Three *weeks*. It's insane. I wasn't even sure if I liked him after three weeks." We ambled to an open table and sat by the window overlooking the beach.

When I asked her if a part of her wanted the pain, I wasn't entirely surprised by her resistance. But then she stopped, set down her paper cup, and a shocked look spread across her face.

She groaned. "You're right. I'm giving this relationship more meaning than it should have, and I'm doing it by holding onto the pain. It's like if the breakup hurts more, then the relationship meant more. But it should be the other way around."

Her realization was an Ace of Swords moment.

The Symbols

From a numerological perspective, ones are about beginnings and creation. And as the first card in its suit, the Ace of Swords contains these elements as well. The teardrop shaped Hebrew-letter *yods* floating above the sword's handle represent new beginnings and the possibility of energy made manifest. But being swords, this card comes with a mental twist.

From a bank of storm clouds symbolizing confused thinking, a hand extends an upright, double-edged sword spearing a crown (mastery and attainment) draped in palm and olive branches (severity and mercy, respectively). Clarity is breaking through the clouds.

My friend left the café looking more cheerful. She went home and journaled on her epiphany.

Three weeks later, she called me up. "Now that I've let go of that relationship, everything's changed for the better." For her, the Ace of Swords was a beginning, and a transformative one.

What Does This Card Mean for You?

What situation might you need to look at differently? Dig deeper. The answers are there.[1]

---

1. You're right. You're RIGHT. And I know you weren't talking to me when you wrote this, but I need to dig deeper. Why did my father do it? I have to know, or at least try to make sense of all this. Maybe I'm trying to fool myself into believing that if I understood, his suicide would hurt less. I know I should just feel the feeling, but this feeling is too much. - T

Two of Swords

STALEMATE. CROSSROADS. DIVIDED LOYALTIES. *Tough decisions.* Avoidance. Conformity.

"You would not *believe* what he said next about NFTs."

I put the phone on speaker, set it on my reading table, and walked to the tearoom kitchen. Taking my time, I acquired a cup of Earl Grey and a lemon scone. When I returned to my reading room, my friend was still ranting, and I still had only a vague idea what an NFT *was*.

Two of my friends are no longer friends over NFTs and crypto outrage. I'm now avoiding them both. I don't know what compelled me to answer the phone when one called.

Maybe avoidance is cowardice on my part. But I'm tired of them trying to convince me to be on their team, especially when each team is so stridently ideological.

It's made me think a lot lately about loyalty. Particularly loyalty to ideas, and how that loyalty can turn those ideas into ideologies. When is it time to take the blindfold off and reassess our beliefs about ourselves, about others, and about the world we live in?

I'd like to always live with the metaphorical blindfold off. But that's not reality. Most of the day, we're on autopilot, running the same programs over and over without giving them too much thought, because who has t he *time*?

It's all very Two of Swords. One of the questions this card asks us to consider is where we've blinded ourselves, what we're not seeing. It asks if it's time to put down our ideas (those two swords), to get up, and to change position.

The Symbols

The woman on the card holds two swords. They're obviously too big for her. It can't be easy to hold them up like that with her arms crossed.

Her back is to the water, and a waxing crescent moon hangs overhead — both symbols of the unconscious. And our blind spots generally *are* hidden by our unconscious. They're the things we don't want to look at, our shadow. But the burden of not looking at them, of not ripping off the blindfold, not putting down those swords, grows heavier over time. Examination—as scary and painful as it may be—is *worth* it.

If you are at a stalemate, have reached a crossroads, or are avoiding a tough decision, this card suggests a re-examination of assumptions. Check your premises. Once the blindfold is off, an entirely new way of approaching the situation may become obvious.

What Does This Card Mean for You?

As my two ex-friends descend into more extreme positions, I continue to back away, stay out of it, keep my mouth shut. After all, what do I know or care about NFTs?

But by doing that, am I betraying myself? Have I shattered a loyalty to my own principles of honest and forthright dealing? Maybe I've got a blindfold to remove too.[1]

---

1. Mystics attempt to transform themselves so they can perceive the word differently, so they can see the Divine. It's one way to break the stalemate.

I was up most of last night changing my own vision by meditating on the Aces. I can't just let things happen to me anymore. I need to take action. I'm just not sure what action. - T

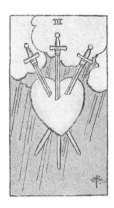

THREE OF SWORDS

HEARTBREAK. MIND OVER EMOTION. *Taking responsibility for your own joy.*

December in the post office. You know the scene. A line that extends out the door. Customers with packages who haven't filled out forms correctly. A single staffer working the desk, and of *course* it's the red-headed, helpful, Chatty Cathy who cheerfully extends the time you're standing there.

Her elderly customer was having trouble working the touchscreen. A frustrated and equally elderly man shouted from his place in line, "The pen! Use the pen!"

Suddenly, the hilarity of the scene descended, and my boredom and impatience fled in a burst of mirth. I was in a Christmas comedy, and I couldn't stop grinning at my fellow actors in the piece.

And here's the *really* weird thing.

It was contagious.

I struck up a conversation with the fascinating old lady in front of me. Other customers began chatting and laughing and smiling. We all still wanted to get out of there. (I was only on time for my lunch date because the person I was meeting was late). But by the time I'd neared the front of the line, my conversational partner was showing me photos of her grandkids. And I was happy to see them.

And that's the Three of Swords.

The Symbols

I've heard lots of different interpretations of this Tarot card, an illustration of a heart pierced by three swords. The most obvious one is heartbreak, and I've included it as a definition here, because sometimes the obvious ones are right.[1]

But let's break this card down. What's going on here? Swords are thoughts. Hearts (or cups) represent emotions. Rain (water, which also represents emotions) is pouring from clouds (another symbol for thoughts). Thoughts and emotions are dripping together. They influence each other.

Think gloomy thoughts? Your emotions will match.

But the good news is you have the power to think positive thoughts and feel joyful emotions. Or at least to stop thinking negative thoughts that trigger you. YOU HAVE THE POWER. (Say it like a muscular cartoon hero. Seriously.)

What Does This Card Mean for You?

The Three of Swords asks us to consider what mental narratives are running through our heads. Are we running ourselves down? Telling ourselves defeatist stories? Imagining awful things *other* people are thinking? STOP THAT.

Seriously. Stop it.

And the first step in stopping is to recognize you're doing it. Recognize what narratives you're telling yourself, and then change them.

What would the situation be like if you were running more positive narratives in your head instead?[2]

---

1. THANK YOU!!!

2. Easy to say, Hyperion... So easy to say. My meditations of late have been difficult. But I keep trying, waiting for an answer. - T

Four of Swords

Retreat. Relaxation. Solitude. Stillness.

Last weekend, I escaped to Donner Lake in the Sierra Nevadas. But I couldn't escape the smoke from the west coast's raging wildfires.[1] It whitened the sky and blurred the pines.

Despite the acrid scent mixing with the sweet smell of sugar pines, the lake had its usual relaxing effect on me. The ocean is relaxing too, but there's something quieter and stiller about a lake. A passing motor may make the waves slap more loudly against the shore, but after half a dozen crashes the waves subside again to their gentle rhythm. (Yes, there's a bigger metaphor here).

But I nearly didn't escape the demon that's been pursuing me for months, namely the torrent of stimulus from the internet. I'd brought my laptop with me to do some lakeside work, thinking the fresh environment would inspire. Soon, but not soon enough, I closed the laptop.

My brain relaxed with the susurration of the waves. All I wanted to do was sit and study the play of light on water. My mind went to stillness, and

---

1. MY wildfires?

I became fully present. I was *at the lake*, and what a waste to be tapping on my keyboard instead of getting *in* the water.

Arguing loudly, two stellar jays alighted in a nearby pine. They hopped from branch to branch and resolved nothing. (And yes, this too is a metaphor, but it also really happened). Smiling, I observed them until they flew deeper into the pines. Then I stripped down and went swimming. A Canadian goose paddled over to bob companionably beside me.

The Symbols

The Four of Swords shows a tomb effigy beneath a stained glass window. Three swords hang on the wall above the effigy, and a fourth stretches beneath it. While at first glance this may seem a little dire, this card is actually about rest.

Swords represent our thoughts, and the Four of Swords invites us to give them a break. To step away and still our minds, to retreat, to relax. It calls us to step out of that whirling hamster wheel of brain activity, because stillness when combined with presence is the key to right action. Sometimes clarity comes when you step away from the problem, but your brain has to step away from the problem too. You *can't* come at things fresh or gain clarity if you're constantly cycling through the same thoughts. [2]

What Does This Card Mean for You?

___

2. I decided to relax last night with a glass of wine and a fire in the woodstove. I went to bed early.

The crow saved me. Which goes to show you never really know the impact of your actions. He woke me with a vicious beak to the forehead.

I was angry, dizzy, and headachy. I needed to let the damn crow out of the house. But I had to crawl to the door to do it.

This should have been a warning sign, but I was too confused. I managed to get the door open, and then I guess I passed out. I woke up to find my brother standing over me and the crow gone.

Charles was surprisingly kind for someone who thought I'd passed out drunk. We'd both seen enough of that from our father and our tolerance is low. He helped get me inside, made me another cup of tea, and sat me down for a long conversation about the estate. He offered to manage my share as a conservatorship, since it was obvious I didn't want to deal with that stuff. I refused. I don't want to deal with it, but step up I will. - T

Let your mind be still as a summer lake beneath a cloudless sky. How can you make a retreat work for you?[3]

---

3. Four of Swords Meditation:
   Breathe in stillness.
   Breathe out and relax.
   Breathe in and be present.
   Breathe out and relax.
   Breathe in and feel.
   Feel the air on your skin.
   Feel your breath moving in and out of your lungs.
   Feel your body.
   Breathe in and be present.
   Breathe out and enjoy the moment.
   Breathe in presence.
   Breathe out and feel the moment.
   Breathe in and know all you need is now.
   Breathe out and relax knowing you are safe.
   Breathe in stillness.
   Breathe out and relax.

   -T

FIVE OF SWORDS

COMPETITION. CONFLICT. COMPARISON WITH *others. Loss. Concern with others' behavior.*

Tarot readers can be as competitive, backbiting, and snipey as any other group of humans. I'm ashamed to say I once had a Tarot archrival of my own. I won't mention his name. We came up in the same psychic f airs.

Unlike me, who went on to have a small but fulfilling practice, he built an online empire. And then he lobbied the town to require other Tarot readers to get fortune-telling licenses. Easy for *him* to get one—he had plenty of money plus a lawyer to deal with the paperwork. The way many of us saw it, he was basically pulling up the ladder behind him.

Ultimately, he failed. Long story. High drama. Never mind why. But my jaw still tightens when I think of him. I'm not proud of it, because my remembered annoyance says more about me than him.

The brutal truth? When I thought about his success, deep down I worried I'd come up short. And that's no way to live. Also, I can't control how other people behave. It's wrong to try. But the situation was a good representation of what's going on in the Five of Swords.

The Symbols

A man stands on a shore holding three swords. Two more swords lie at his feet. He smirks like a jerk at two men walking away. Though we can't see the other men's faces, one holds his head in his hands as if he's weeping.

You can't always win. People are going to be more successful than you. But there's no sense dwelling on it. Better to be the guy with his jacket slung over his shoulder and walking away. He lost his sword, but he's not crying about it. He's moving on. And maybe he's figured out that even without his sword, he's right where he's supposed to be. Disarmed but standing, and walking toward his own future, the future that's right for *him*.

What Does This Card Mean for You?

This card asks us to consider how we may be comparing ourselves to others. Are you being the best person *you* can be? Or are you dwelling on the way other people *should* be?

And don't be the sore winner with the swords. No one likes that guy.[1]

---

1. In the bright light of morning, I realized something was off about last night. I'd only had one glass of wine. I checked the wood stove. A wad of singed paper partially blocked the chimney. I can't figure out how the paper got jammed up there. It's amazing the carbon monoxide didn't kill me. - T

Six of Swords

JOURNEY. TRANSITION. PASSAGE FROM *rough times to smooth. Going with the flow.*

Opening Beanblossom's Tea and Tarot was a passage through the underworld. Murder. Mayhem. Misunderstandings and mistakes. (We found a dead body behind the tearoom. Don't ask.) It felt like we'd never get Beanblossom's open.

I'm not sure how I got through the drama. Actually, I *do* know. The Six of Swords card got me through. It gave me hope and let me know the rough times would end.

The Symbols

The Six of Swords shows a huddled woman and child being ferried across a body of water. On one side of the boat, the water is rough. On the far side of the boat, the water is smooth. Six swords stand upright in the boat, and the woman looks through the cluster of swords. Worried thoughts are at the front of her mind.

But she's moving into smooth waters.[1] The big question is, are the swords making leaks in the boat? How much trouble will our own anxieties create as we work through our problems? Odds are, they're not helpful.

Fortunately, the ferryman has got his eyes on the far shore as he paddles steadily toward it.

What Does This Card Mean for You?

How can you get out of your head and be the ferryman, pushing forward, eyes on the prize, rather than sunk in worry? Because this is a card of hope. Have faith you're moving toward better things, because you are.

FYI, there were a few more bumps along the road to Beanblossom's, but we're in a good groove now. Plus I get all the scones I can eat.[2]

---

1. There's a quote from the I Ching that reminds me of this card: "It furthers one to cross the great water." Water symbolizes the emotions as well as consciousness. The implication here may be a crossing of psychic territory. - T

2. The police came to see me today. They seem to think my father's death wasn't an accident and it wasn't suicide either. It was murder. And even though we'd never really gotten along, I felt like the world had been jerked from beneath my feet. - T

Murder. It was murder. My father was murdered. This changes everything.

SEVEN OF SWORDS

CLEVERNESS. TRICKERY. DECEIT. ILLUSION. *Deception. Avoiding responsibility.*

Once, when I was leaving a rennaisance faire, a crow tried to snatch a shiny ornament off my cloak. The ornament was well fastened, so both of us departed dissatisfied by the encounter.

It was a Seven of Swords moment, the crow dazzled by the flash of the ornament, and me shocked by its sneak attack. Hot with embarrassment, I slunk to my Jeep.

There are no birds in the Seven of Swords card, though they litter the rest of this suit. Sometimes they're mere dots in the distance. But they're there, because birds are symbols of air. And like thoughts, they can vanish quickly, or travel to dark or sunny realms.

The Symbols

In this card, a man carrying seven swords tiptoes from an encampment, a symbol of power and society. He's commonly believed to be a thief, and the Seven of Swords a card of deception. But he could also be a deserter.

Crows are clever birds, and I like but do not trust them. The card could warn of someone attempting to deceive. But this is the swords suit, which focuses on thoughts and ideas. Is this card warning of self-deception?

What Does This Card Mean for You?

Sometimes the easy path is the wrong one—for ourselves and others. What are you evading?[1]

---

1. There's a myth about the language of birds. Once you understand it, the mysteries of the universe are unlocked. Perhaps it's a metaphor for learning the language of our own thoughts, to learn the true and steady grammar of our being and so avoid mental missteps.

How to Learn the Language of Birds

Watch a crow spiral in the sky,
And leave shiny toys for a magpie.
Light a stick of incense,
And contemplate its smoky coils.
Study the shapes of clouds,
And muse their meanings.
Feel the wind across your skin,
And listen, listen, listen.

-T

EIGHT OF SWORDS

THE PRISON OF OUR *minds. Victim mentality. Feeling trapped. Crisis. Self-imposed limitations.*

Are you ready for a confession?

Last night, I went to a party and planted my foot directly into my mouth.

It was one of those swank affairs with money men and glamshackle women and buckets of champagne.

It might be because of the latter that I didn't realize my faux pas until the man I'd been talking to walked away. I went home thinking about it and thinking about it and finally called to apologize.

He had no idea what I was talking about.

Of *course.*

I'd been overthinking my presumed faux pas. My worrying had ruined my evening *and* most of the next morning. And all for nothing.

The Symbols

In the Eight of Swords, a bound and blindfolded prisoner is surrounded by eight swords, stuck upright in the rocky ground. The swords don't make a very secure prison though. The captive could easily make her way through... if the blindfold was off.

But that's the problem. It's hard to see through the barrier when what's blocking you is in your own head. Like my obsession about having spoken in a less than stellar fashion at that party.

Last night's case of the Eight of Swords is only a mild example. But when thoughts get in our own way, it can be debilitating.

- That acquaintance of yours who's so certain they can't succeed that they never try.

- The pessimist friend who expects disaster, so problems are ALL they ever see.

- And don't get me started on that person who over complicates EVERYTHING and then wonders why it's so hard to get things done.

What Does This Card Mean for You?

When this card appears in a Tarot reading, it's an opportunity to try to figure out what thoughts are blocking you. Or turned another way, you have a problem (everyone does). How are your own thoughts contributing to it?[1]

---

1. I received your email today. Your prod asking when I'd be finished with the edits was laughably gentle. But I needed your reminder. Not only to keep plugging away with your manuscript, but the reminder that real-world results require real-world action. I can't meditate my way out of being a murder suspect (though meditation has kept me from hyperventilating). I've been bound up by my old patterns and beliefs. I've become so used to just letting things unfold that I forgot I'm part of that unfolding. The answers are at my father's house. I'm going there tonight. -T

NINE OF SWORDS

Never read the morning news. This morning I had some spare time and made *that* mistake. And though I kept telling myself hysteria sells and headlines are to be taken with a heaping of salt, I closed my computer with a sense of doom and gloom. It haunted me the rest of the day.

But here's the thing. My day was actually pretty good. I saw a stream of pleasant clients. My partner in the tearoom had a new scone recipe for me to taste-test. I'm healthy. I've got friends. I've got a roof over my head.

And no one knows the future with one hundred percent certainty. Yes, bad things might come. But they might not. And in the here and now, life was good.

In short, the sense that everything was wrong was *all in my mind.*

The mind. Thoughts. The intellect... Swords. Specifically, the Nine of Swords.

The Symbols

The Nine of Swords depicts a woman waking from a nightmare, nine swords hanging over her head. Her thoughts created the nightmare. They aren't real things. This card doesn't necessarily predict disaster in the real world.[1] It diagnoses or predicts *anxiety*. That's internal, not external.

Interestingly, in this card, the woman *isn't* trapped in her dream. She's sitting up and awake. She's still shaken, her head in her hands. But the nightmare is over. She now needs to get out of bed and get going.

What Does This Card Mean for You?

This card tells us not to let our fears dominate us or hold us back. Fear can help us avoid danger. Anxiety can warn us to take action. But otherwise, fear and anxiety are useless. More often they trap us in a cycle of hopelessness, and at their extremes, in delusion and histrionics. They need to be dealt with.

But here's the tough part: when we're in a nightmare, we usually don't know it. All we can do to break free is to seriously ask ourselves: *is this real?*

Is this real?[2]

---

1. But sometimes, it does. - T

2. I didn't go to my father's house. No, this wasn't me being chicken shit. When I went to grab my car keys, I discovered my second set of keys was missing. I turned the cottage upside down looking for them. They're not here. Is it possible that the cops weren't lying when they said my car had been seen at the house? Could someone have taken it the night my father died? But then why not return the keys? And once I started thinking that, the newspaper in the chimney seemed... Could that have been intentional? Is this real? - T

TEN OF SWORDS

A HARD ENDING. DRAMA *queen. Loss. Pain. Betrayal.*

I don't often draw cards for myself. Sure, I do a card of the day, but that's more to keep my intuition and understanding locked in than because I want a reading.

But that day I wanted a reading. For weeks I'd been in a flirtation with someone who I thought might matter. I was making myself crazy. It was all I could think about. I couldn't focus on work. I couldn't focus when I was out with friends.

Finally, I drew a Celtic Cross spread for myself. It was enlightening. But the real surprise came in position eight, the "environment" of the situation. It was the Ten of Swords.

The Symbols

Now the Ten of Swords is usually about loss, betrayal, and challenging endings. It's a Tarot card as dark as the black clouds in the background of the dead man with the swords in his back.

But I wasn't feeling dark when I drew that card. The fact is, I hadn't been interested in love like *that* in a long time. I'd been too busy focusing on my work, my health, myself to put in the effort of connecting with someone special. And I'd been having *fun* on my own.

But when I saw that card, I realized how cold and closed my heart had become until this person had come into my life. Even if the flirtation went nowhere, it was a gift that had opened my heart.

Then I remembered something an older and wiser Tarot reader had told me about that card: "Ten swords in his back. Isn't that a little *much*? A bit of *overkill*?"

I turned my focus to the swords themselves, symbols of the mind. I realized yes, this *was* my environment. The environment of the situation was the inside of my head. I'd been living in darkness for the last few weeks, playing out scenarios of things going right and things going wrong, and frankly being a drama queen about it all.

I needed a mental change of scene. And whenever I caught myself thinking about the what-ifs of the situation, I remembered that card. It helped. (FYI, the key card in that reading was the Ace of Cups, so you probably have a good idea where all this led).

But enough about me. Let's talk about what's going on in *your* head. If you draw this card, here are some things to remember. First, notice the man's odd hand gesture? It's a mudra, sealing off or ending the energy.

Next, the sun is rising. This may be an ending, but though the worst is over, *you* are not. The sky (like the suit in general) represents the mental state of the seeker, and the clouds in it are black, representing mourning, confusion, or darkness.

I don't usually go to the astrological associations—my mother's an astrophysicist and despises astrology. But I think it's interesting with this card: the Sun in Gemini.

The Sun represents the center of our identity and consciousness. It symbolizes courage, will, and leading with its heart. The Sun can also represent our mission in life, our core purpose for being. The Sun is associated with the father and the day principle. Like Leo, which it rules, the Sun represents charisma, confidence, and creative flair. Ill-aspected or taken to extreme, the Sun can manifest itself as self-centeredness.

Gemini belongs to the element air and is ruled by Mercury, the planet of change, communication, and commerce. Gemini symbolizes curiosity, imagination, information, and communication. The sign can also represent the adaptability and openness of the human mind, or taken to the extreme, doing too much at once and causing confusion.

Putting the two together: The Ten of Swords can represent that the seeker has the courage and will (the Sun) to change (Gemini) the situation. Or you're being a drama queen. In either case, you *do* have the ability to cope.[1]

What Does This Card Mean for You?

How can you pick yourself up and start over?

Because you're going to be okay.

---

1. I've been served. My brother wants to put me under involuntary financial conservatorship like that pop star who lived under her father's control for years. My brother would control all my finances due to my "mental limitations." He's saying I'm crazy.

   I'm trying not to panic. Just because I'm an eccentric who prefers living in the woods to a luxury mansion filled with vipers doesn't mean I'm insane. Charles doesn't know about my voluntary commitment though. Can he? - T

Page of Swords

Analyzing problems. Mental turmoil. *Figuring things out.*

I've had plenty of bad moments. We all have.

When I was younger during those dark times, I'd go up on the roof to figure things out. Being above the world, seeing things from a different point of view, helped clear my mind.

Or at least it used to. After a certain nighttime incident on my parents' roof, I stopped.

Now, I turn to my Tarot deck. When I'm reading the cards, the real world falls away. It's just me and a pack of archetypal images, symbols jogging my brain, making me face my life and my beliefs from a different perspective.

Those moments of seeking, of trying to figure stuff out, are what the Page of Swords is all about.

The Symbols

The page's hair and tunic are being blown sideways. The grass is being flattened by the wind, as are the palms in the background. This rushing of air can symbolize either a burst of ideas or mental turbulence. There are, of course, more air signs in the card, like the puffy cartoon clouds filling a sky sprinkled with birds. But you get the picture.

All that mental energy and in the hands of a youth.

Though he's stepping forward, the Page of Swords looks backward, over one shoulder. He hasn't reached clarity yet. He's poised at an in-between stage, in a pause, in a break. And he needs to be careful with that oversized sword. Did he "borrow" it from the knight?

All of the Tarot's pages are of the earth. And there are earth symbols in the card as well, like the grassy knoll he stands upon. The Page of Swords is on the cusp of bringing the mental power of the Swords into real-world, practical use.

What Does This Card Mean for You?

Now is the time to focus. You can make your ideas real, but you might want to take a step back and do a quick review to make sure it's a completely matured idea first.

How can you bring more clarity to the situation?[1]

---

1. Honestly, I have no idea. I'm not a forensic scientist. - T

KNIGHT of SWORDS .

KNIGHT OF SWORDS

Outspoken. Quick thinking. Ambitious. *Logical.*

Chaining myself to a pier piling while dressed like a 19th century aristocrat might *not* have been the best way to attract attention to my cause. Especially since I'd accidentally dropped the padlock key into the ocean.

But it got attention. And we managed to defeat the proposed city licensing requirement for Tarot readers. There is some question as to how my stunt on the pier affected the outcome. But drastic times, drastic measures, etc., etc.

I'd like to think it was a Knight of Swords moment of logical, decisive action. The problem is, like all the Court Cards, the Knight's traits come with a dark side. An outspoken nature can turn critical and obnoxious. Quick thinking can become impulsive. Ambitious can become ego driven. And logic can turn cold.

The Symbols

In the card, we see the airy symbols of the sword suit—flying birds, butterfly and bird ornamentation, the wing on the knee joint of armor, windblown clouds and trees, the feather plume and billowing cloak.

We also see fire symbols for the action-oriented knights—the dry landscape, the fiery shape of the horse's mane, and the red plume and the cloak. Put it all together, and you get swift motion, action, and intellect.

What Does This Card Mean for You?

Now is the time for swift, decisive, and logical action. How are the Knight's energies operating in your life? And if they're not, how should they be?[1]

---

1. Not well at all. - T

QUEEN OF SWORDS

Seeking truth. Discernment. Judgment. *Boundaries.*

In Tarot, Court Cards can be the most difficult to interpret. Depending on where they fall in a reading, I look at them as representing a personality in my life, or personality traits that are either working for or against me

.

And so I draw the Queen of Swords. The Queen is smart, she's discerning, and she's got no problem running you through with that sword in her hand. She's all about good judgment and setting healthy boundaries. This Queen's got no qualms about beating you over the head with the flat of her sword if you don't get the message.

I was not feeling like any of that the day I drew this card. I'd just bought a lottery ticket and wasn't sure if I'd make it to the gas station before running out of gas.

She was not me.

But the card was reversed, so it could have meant that energy was being repressed. I needed to metaphorically turn that card around.

So okay. I could use a little more of the Queen in my life, and preferably before my business partner, Abigail, discovered I'd spent this month's marketing budget signing our tearoom up for a Tarot conference. True, Abs will love it, and it will be good for our business.

Also true, I should have discussed it with her first. I also probably shouldn't have written her bio for the conference. But *Abigail Beanblossom is part elf and off the shelf* was definitely more interesting than anything she would have come up with.

She's going to kill me.

On second thought, maybe *Abs* is the Queen of Swords, and this is a warning not to give her the news when she's holding anything pointy?

The Symbols

The Queen of Swords sits on her throne, sword upraised. The fact that she's a queen implies that she's mature. The card is filled with air signs—the clouds, the butterflies, the bird, the wind blowing the trees. Despite the breeze, the Queen's gown is still. In the face of turbulence, she maintains her equilibrium.

But as a queen, she's also of water. The stream flowing through the left side of the card represents her intuition. Added together, she has all the insightfulness and intelligence of the Knight, balanced by her intuition and maturity.

She can have a dark side though. Judgment can turn to vindictiveness. Discernment can morph into being overly picky. Truth seeking can become obsessive.

She wears mourning bracelets on her wrist, which is why she is sometimes viewed as a widow. Butterflies aren't just symbols of air. They also represent transformation. Loss has transformed her, and she's come out strong on the other side of the experience.[1]

What Does This Card Mean for You?

This queen calls on us to temper our sharp edges with compassion. Does this queen represent qualities you need to embody or release?

---

1. And I'll come out of this too. I may not be feeling the Queen of Swords energy now, but I will, someday. - T

KING OF SWORDS

JUDGMENT. MENTAL CLARITY. AUTHORITY. *Law. Truth. Intellect.*

Yesterday morning I drew the King of Swords and immediately knew what it meant—a certain detective of my acquaintance was going to be a big part of my day.

He's tough. He's smart. He's no-nonsense. And he's *all* about law and order and bringing bad guys to justice. That takes a measure of mental acuity. He's not only able to follow the breadcrumbs to the truth, but he *gets* human nature, with all its flaws and foibles.

He's also a bit of a germaphobe, which is *not* an attribute of the King of Swords. But nobody's perfect.

And then... I didn't hear a peep from the detective all day.

What I did encounter was:

- My business partner confronting me with a budget I'd blown through and forcing me to figure out how to fix it. And I did. It was painful (I hate math and budgets), but I did it.

- A client who'd committed a minor crime and needed to find a path to redemption (confessing and taking the consequences); and

THE MYSTERIES OF TAROT

- A near speeding ticket. After the above reading with my client, I was pulled over on 101. I immediately fessed up, admitted everything, and the CHP officer let me off with a warning.

So that's two lessons. First, don't assume when it comes to Tarot. Sometimes you know, and sometimes you just *think* you know. Second, the Court Cards can represent a person, or they can represent the energies or attributes of that card at play in your life.... Or that *should* be at play.

In the first case, I needed to step up and act like the King of Swords. In the second, my client did. And in the third, the CHP had all the law and authority behind him. All I could do was tell the truth like a King, and it set me free.

The Symbols

Like the Emperor, the King of Swords faces directly from the card. He holds a double-edged sword, but he holds it at an angle, showing a willingness to compromise. You may not *like* what he's going to do with it, but whatever it is, he'll be fair.

Clouds billow in the background. Kings are of air and so are swords, making this King the master of reason and logic. *Brrr...*[1]

So if you draw this in a reading, step up. Be the King. Even if the card does mean you're going to encounter someone else like him that day, adding some positive King of Swords energy to your life is good for the soul. And the pocketbook.

What Does This Card Mean for You?

The King of Swords is the most powerful member of the suit and has the most authority and control. He also represents the most developed expression and successful example of his suit, which is Air—the mental realm. How can you use this king's energies to improve the situation?

---

1. I suppose you're implying the King's dark side here? You might want to be more explicit: someone who puts ideas over people, cold and cruel. - T

THE SUIT OF CUPS

WATER
Emotions
Subconscious
Ebbing and Flowing
The Tides[1]
The Moon

---

1. It nourishes our thirst, and it drowns. - T

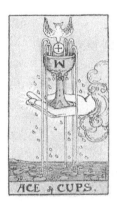

ACE OF CUPS

NEW LOVE. NEW RELATIONSHIP. *Awakening of cosmic consciousness. Channel for spirit. Gratitude.*

It's a little depressing how often I've drawn the Ace of Cups. Aces are about beginnings and initiation, and cups about emotions and love. So for me this card has usually indicated a new relationship, though not necessarily a lasting one. Until one day, when the relationship this Tarot card was nudging me toward had zero to do with romance.

I'd been reading Tarot for a couple years by that point. I knew the classic meanings, I could put them together, and I was even starting more intuitive work with clients. I was doing (and still do) my own daily Tarot card reading—just one card. That day, I'd drawn the Ace of Cups. And though I wasn't expecting a good day, the Ace gave me a lift of hope.

Its meaning unfolded later that day. I was in the hospital visiting my aunt. We'd been taking her there on an almost weekly basis after a cancer diagnosis—I won't go into the details. But she'd been coming down with one infection after another, with no end in sight.

I was bored, sitting outside the examination room. So although the spring day was drizzly, I wandered to the balcony garden outside. At the moment, the clouds parted, and a sunbeam struck the ocean. The light glimmered, the ocean whitening around it.

And suddenly, I knew. My aunt was going to be okay.

I returned inside. The doctor emerged from the exam room and told us my aunt was in remission.

It was my first knowing. My first true connection. Did I channel? Did I forge some connection with the universal mind?

I'm still baffled. Until that moment, the idea of awakening cosmic consciousness in myself had been entirely theoretical. There are some things you can't entirely understand until you experience them.

I'm still not sure I *do* understand. I don't have these moments of insight on tap. My knowings don't come on command. But they do still occasionally come.

Aces. Someone once told me that the first card in the suit contains all the energy of that suit. In that moment at the hospital, I felt all the energy of the Cups—intuition, spirit, connection—flowing through me. I was initiated that day by something bigger than myself.[1]

---

1. Adelaide came to the cottage today with her latest rescue (a Chihuahua). She'd learned about my brother's threatened conservatorship and wants to help. I'm grateful.

   She told me Charles has been trying to get more control of our father's company for years. I had no idea it mattered to him that much. He's been the Chief Financial Officer since last spring. I'd assumed he was on track to take the company over, and I would have been happy to let him. I don't care about managing the money or the company. But I don't want to be on an allowance at my brother's mercy either. At least my sister, for all her faults, is on my side.

   After she left, something odd happened. Despite all my fear and anger, my heart broke open and I fell in love. I'm not sure who I'm in love with. I'm alone in the woods. There's no one to attach this feeling to. But I can't shake this happy, bubbling, excited feeling in my chest. Is this union with nature? The Divine? Maybe it doesn't matter. I'm h appy. - T

The Symbols

A golden chalice floats above a pool dotted with water lilies, the latter representing eternal life. Five streams (representing the five senses?) overflow from the cup.

The cup is commonly believed to represent the Holy Grail from Arthurian legend. In the story of the knight Parcival, a dove magically empowers the Grail, and in this card, a dove with a communion-type wafer dives toward the cup. The cup also resembles a baptismal font, implying a spiritual initiation.

What Does This Card Mean for You?

How can you be that over-flowing chalice? Because it's by being loving that we attract love of all kinds to us.

TWO OF CUPS

LOVE. PASSION. CONNECTION. A *marriage or proposal. A partnership.*

Last month, my friend Jay wandered into my office looking low. "I'm done with love. I'm done trying. I'm done getting my hopes up. I'm going to die alone, and that's fine."

It didn't look like it was really fine with him. And though he said he hadn't come for a reading, he didn't say "no" when I offered one.

I drew the Two of Cups. "It looks like you're in exactly the right frame of mind to find love."

Jay folded his arms. "You do realize sarcasm is the lowest form of humor."

"I wasn't being sarcastic. I mean it."

"How is this helping?"

"People can sense when we're *trying*. We have to not try and just be, and sometimes that means letting the dreams and desires go so they'll unfold on their own, the way they're meant to. And it seems like you've accomplished that."

Jay laughed caustically. "I told you, I'm over it." And then he left.

You can probably guess what happened. He returned to my office last week, and he'd fallen in love with an amazing woman who loved him back.

No, the Two of Cups isn't always about romantic love. It can be about passion for a project, or about a business partnership. But the Cups are cards of the emotions, so emotions are typically somehow in play when this card appears.

The Symbols

A man and woman toast each other in a pledge. Watching over the pair is a winged, lion-headed Aeon of eternity from the Roman mystery cult of Mithras, god of mutual obligation. Beneath the Aeon hovers a caduceus, an alchemical symbol of what is created when forces are combined.

This is a card of long-lasting, positive partnership of all sorts—love, business, and friendship.

What Does This Card Mean for You?

What (or who) are you passionate about? This card is a sign that there's possibility for growth here, if you take it.[1]

---

1. I explored my father's house, looking for clues like an overgrown Hardy Boy. Ha. And of course I found nothing. The police have already scoured the place, and I'm no detective. There was no sign on the balcony of a struggle. No incriminating documents in his study, lined with books with fancy spines he never opened.

   As I was leaving, I surprised my stepmother and her driver, Gabriel, in the garage. Imagine a space designed like an English squire's barn, but with parking spots rather than stalls. It's a nice enough place for a romantic rendezvous. And judging from what I saw, it wasn't the first such assignation between Joan and Gabriel. - T

THREE OF CUPS

EMOTIONAL SUPPORT. CELEBRATION. COLLABORATION. *Success.*

A client I hadn't seen in six months — let's call her Marla — turned up in my office looking fabulous. She'd not only dropped forty pounds, but she'd gotten off the blood pressure meds she'd been taking for years. She glowed. But there was a furrow between her brows.

I kicked back and laced my hands behind my head. "Hey, girl. What's happening?"

She dropped heavily into the highbacked chair opposite. "I just got back from visiting friends in Seattle, and they were..." She hesitated.

"Damp?" I asked. "Shadowy? Depressed?"

"Really down on me," Marla fumed. "All they could talk about was everything that was *wrong* with my new exercise program. It was too hard. It was even dangerous. By losing weight I was fat shaming others. I worked with a doctor to get off those damn blood pressure pills. There was nothing dangerous about it. I can walk up the stairs to my apartment without breaking a sweat now."

"Honey," I said, "you deserve better friends. Because what you accomplished is amazing."

She'd had a massive success—a lifechanging one. She needed to celebrate it. Fortunately, she *did* have better friends closer to home, people she could lean on for support and cheerleading.

The Symbols

Three dancing women toast each other. On the ground nearby are harvest fruits—symbols of abundance. This is a card celebrating success.

But since it's Cups and, therefore, about emotions, it's also about the emotional side of that success. These ladies are not just celebrating for themselves. They're building each other up with their toasts.

What Does This Card Mean for You?

In a reading, the Three of Cups represents a positive outcome—what do you have to celebrate?

But it also asks, how can you help the people in your life celebrate *their* wins, big and small?[1]

---

1. I woke up last night on alert, my heart pounding and not knowing why. And then I heard it, a faint rustling inside the cottage. I lay in my narrow bed, my eyes open and unmoving. But whoever was in here was out of my range of vision.

   Slowly, I turned my head. And saw no one. The rustling noise came again. I got up and turned on the light beside my bed. The sound stopped.

   I walked through the cottage - it's only one room, so this didn't take long. There was no question but I was alone. And then I heard the rustling again, coming from beneath the wood stove. It was still giving off some heat.

   I knelt to peer beneath it. Two beady black eyes stared back. I'm ashamed to say I yelled and fell on my ass before realizing it was a squirrel. He vanished into the small woodpile beside the stove. Too tired to deal with the problem, I returned to bed. I managed to get him out of the cabin the next morning, but I still have no idea how he got inside. - T

Four of Cups

Reevaluation. Imaginary problems. Discontent. *Cutting oneself off from opportunity.*

I wanted my own Tarot room. I'd been dreaming about it for years. I'd found the perfect location. I'd even found the perfect building (or so I'd thought).

And then I discovered my realtor was a con man, and he'd leased the building to someone else—a woman named Abigail who'd planned on starting up a tearoom there.

Total disaster.

I was furious—at the so-called realtor, at myself, even at poor Abigail, who'd been taken for even more money than I had. I was a grown man and wanted my Tarot room, dammit.

It took me a while to realize I'd been offered something even better—a business partner who had a better head for (and interest in) numbers than me. Plus, a tearoom offered a built-in market for walk-in trade *and* the ability to serve food to my clients.

Beanblossom's Tea and Tarot was born. But I spent more time than I'd like to admit resisting the idea. I'd been like that guy in the Four of Cups, arms crossed, stubbornly refusing the offered gift.

The Symbols

A hand extends from a cloud and offers a cup to a man seated beneath a tree. Three more cups sit by the man's feet.

Does he even notice the offered cup? Or is he too busy studying the cups on the ground before him? After all, they're in excellent condition. Why not take the cups that are, well, normal? Why take the oddball cup at the end of a disembodied hand?

Cups are about emotions, so if this person is cutting himself off from what's offered, why? Does he feel safer sticking with what he knows? Is he emotionally attached to those three cups on the ground?

What Does This Card Mean for You?

This card not only asks what opportunities we might be ignoring, but *why*. And more importantly, how can we open ourselves up and get out of our own way?

We're being offered a gift. Now we just have to expand our vision to see it.[1]

---

1. I spoke to my lawyer today. He says the conservatorship has a chance. I'm in trouble, Hyperion. Real trouble. - T

FIVE OF CUPS

LOSS. REGRET. DISAPPOINTMENT. FAILURE.

"I didn't get the job." In my office, Sam sagged in the red-velvet chair opposite. "And I really thought I'd aced that interview."

"What did you do?" I asked.

"Do?" He laughed hollowly and rubbed his chest. "I spent the rest of the week playing video games and eating takeout. *This* was the job I wanted. It's my dream job. I've trained for it. If I can't get this job, what hope have I got in the industry?"

It was a Five of Cups moment.

The Symbols

A figure cloaked in black stands on a riverbank. He studies three overturned cups. Two cups remain upright behind him.

Can he stop dwelling on the loss, turn around, and focus on what's left? There's a bridge crossing the river. If he can take the lessons and move on, he could reach the castle on the opposite bank. But he seems to be stuck, dwelling on those fallen cups.

This card asks us to evaluate what failures or regrets are holding us back. Have we learned the wrong lessons from them?

Sam was caught in a failure spiral. He'd given up, stuck believing that he was doomed to never succeed. But that wasn't the lesson. There was a reason he hadn't gotten the job, and maybe that reason had nothing to do with him or everything to do with him. But the game wasn't over. Two cups were still standing. And the only thing stopping him from attaining them was his dwelling on the loss.

What Does This Card Mean for You?

What lessons have you learned when things went wrong? Were they the right ones? Or are they the three overturned cups, uselessly holding you back? Isn't it time for you to move on?[1]

---

1. The police searched my cottage today. The squirrel watching from the nearby oak seemed more indignant about it than I was. I'm just... That bubbly feeling is still there in my heart, somewhere. But another part of me feels flattened. I told them about my stepmother and Gabriel. They didn't seem particularly interested or surprised. And is it wrong that I'm more worried about the loss of that feeling than about the fact that the police searched my cabin? They really think I may have killed my own father.

Six of Cups

Revisiting the past. Nostalgia. *Memories.*

My parents are in the process of selling the house I grew up in. I've been driving back and forth from my place to theirs to help with the clean-out. I'm happy they're selling. The house is too big for them now, and it's the right thing to do.

But seeing it go, riffling through old photos and documents and deciding what to keep or toss, has been bittersweet. When I think of "home," this is the house I think of. It's the house I'll probably always think of. It's too full of memories to be otherwise.

Some say nostalgia is a bad thing. That we need to focus on the present. Like so much, it's a matter of balance. The sweetness of the past is something to treasure. We can learn from the past—from both the good and the bad.

But when we dwell on the past, when we cling to it, it can become a chain around our necks, keeping us from moving on. It's like those family documents I mentioned, some over a hundred years old. The family history is interesting... on the rare occasions we look at the old photos and papers. The rest of the time, the boxes clutter up the garage.

Why have *my* parents gotten stuck being the curators of the family museum? All of it will just pass on to my sister and me one day. Then we'll add our own detritus, and on and on.

As I sorted the documents into *stay* or *go* piles, my nostalgia turned to anger. I'm not proud of it. I grew ruthless tossing things out. I'd reached my breaking point. The past had become too crowded with memories and too painful.

The Symbols

In the Six of Cups, a boy hands a girl a chalice filled with white five-pointed flowers. More cups overflowing with the flowers decorate the foreground.

Children represent innocence, as does the color white (and let's not debate whether white's a color or not). Flowers with five petals are associated with memory and also with the suit of pentacles, which relates to being grounded in the physical world. The past is affecting the present.

Upright, this card represents lovely memories. These memories bind us to others. They can be the building blocks for a positive future. Enjoy t hem.

But when this Tarot card is reversed, something's not quite right. It could indicate clinging to the past or taking those memories too far. Or it could indicate that something is blocking you from seeing the past as it truly was.[1]

What Does This Card Mean for You?

Our past will always be a part of us, but it doesn't have to rule us. How is the past operating in the situation now?

---

1. I got the squirrel to eat peanuts out of my hand today. Small victories. He seems to have taken it for granted that the cottage belongs to him now too. - T

SEVEN OF CUPS

Fantasy. Illusion. Sentiment. Wishful *thinking*. *Vision*.

The worst thing I ever did to a relationship was put my partner on a pedestal. At the time, I was so blinded by my own fantasies that I wasn't able to see him clearly. It wasn't fair to him or to me, and the relationship died a hot, disastrous death. It was total cringe.

Imagination can be a wonderful gift. But it can also go horribly wrong, leading us down a path we don't belong on.

The Symbols

The Seven of Cups warns of the perils of fantasy. In the card, some of the cups hold things that *look* good but which on closer inspection might not be. And some of the cups hold terrors like the dragon and the snake. Our imagination can also lead us into anxieties that may never come to fulfillment.

The central cup is unlike the others. From it emerges what looks like a ghost—the spirit of pure vision. Not all of our imaginings are bad. Some can encourage us to strive for high-reaching goals.

What Does This Card Mean for You?

If this card appears in a reading, it asks how the spirit of the Seven of Cups is manifesting in you. Are you seeing the situation clearly or seeing what you want to see? Is your imagination leading you to catastrophize?[1]

---

1. A Stoic concept may apply here: phantasia, which means "appearance" or "perception." The Greek philosopher Epictetus wrote the gods gave man the power to separate reality from appearance (I'm paraphrasing), and this is what differentiates us from the lower animals.

But I keep thinking of your stories. I see the people on these pages in my head, but of course they're not exactly the people you describe. They're a co-creation between the words on the page and my imagination. Life is the same. I interpret reality through my imagination, I co-create my life. And it's real. But if my imagination goes wrong and conjures dragons and castles, my life goes wrong too, growing more distorted. Because my partner in this co-creation, reality, is still underlying it all. The rock I stub my toe on is still a rock.

Last night's vision... I can't describe it. But that's the whole point of the ineffable. I wish I could. I wish I understood what it meant. I wish these vision hangovers weren't attached.

EIGHT OF CUPS

DISAPPOINTMENT. ABANDONMENT. WITHDRAWING. MOVING *on.*

Does absence *really* make the heart grow fonder?

The saying makes zero sense to me. Absence *may* buff out the rough edges of an awful ex's character. We *may* forget the little things about him or her that irritated us. The memory of the guy who abandoned me on a road trip because his spirit guides told him to? It's a hundred percent fading like a bad dream. Distance makes it easier to forgive *and* to forget.

But we also tend to forget the actual *person* as we think of them less and less. And sometimes, occasionally, when we do remember, we think better of them. But is the heart actually growing fonder? Or is it growing more distant? In my experience, it's the latter.

And huzzah for that, because the next thing you know, you've moved on like the guy in the Eight of Cups.

The Symbols

A figure walks away from eight cups standing in the card's foreground. The card is dark and gloomy. Only the moon illuminates the figure's path. A bad news card—right?

Wrong.

Because while disappointment is, well, disappointing, there are times in all our lives when we *need* to move on. It may feel impossible, that the heartbreak or disappointment or failure will never go away. But it does. We keep going, we get past it, and new vistas open before us.

What Does This Card Mean for You?

Let it fade, let it go. How can you move on?[1]

---

1. A simple online search revealed my stepmother has an alibi for my father's death. She and Gabriel were at some society event in San Francisco. There's even a photo of Gabriel handing her out of her limo. I tried to create a scenario where Gabriel returned to the house and killed my father, but the timing just doesn't work. And Shame on me, I really wanted it to be Joan and Gabriel. - T

Nine of Cups

Contentedness. Emotional completeness. Master *of emotions. Gratitude.*

I'm not happy as often as I'd like. Yes, I'm a generally cheerful guy and am all about seizing the day. But I'm rarely *truly* happy. True happiness has only happened a few times in my life.

Once, on vacation at the Grand Canyon, I stood on a cliff, muscles weary and skin damp with sweat from my hike. As the sun set in dusty roses and tangerines, a sense of completeness descended. I was confident, whole, and happy. Maybe even joyful.

I can remember that feeling now, but only distantly. Maybe we're not meant to feel it day-in and day-out. Maybe we need the lows to experience the highs. Or maybe that feeling is reserved for saints and mystics.

The Symbols

But that joy is the satisfied feeling of Tarot's Nine of Cups. It depicts a wealthy man seated beneath a rainbow of cups. His stance is confident and contented. He's got it all.

In numerology, nines symbolize completion and attainment. The man in this card has both of those qualities.

But he's not hanging out in a lush garden like the woman in the Nine of Pentacles, he's surrounded by simple blue curtains. I think this simplicity is one of the keys to this card. True happiness isn't found in *things*. Its foundation is much simpler.

If this card appears in a reading, depending on its position, it could indicate good things are coming. The rainbow shape represents good fortune, after all.

But it's also interesting to consider if you're taking time to enjoy the simple pleasures or if you're overcomplicating things. It could also be a call to reflect on your accomplishments and feel gratitude for all the wonder in your life.

What Does This Card Mean for You?

What goals have you achieved? How can you approach the situation with a sense of abundance?[1]

---

1. People think the Stoics strove to be emotionless and spartan, but it's not true. They strove not to be reactionary, and they did enjoy the good things in life. They just didn't want to become attached to comforts because they understood the transient nature of things (and people). It's why I moved to the woods. Well, part of the reason. My father's wealth isolated him from what mattered. I thought if I could isolate myself, I could find something greater. But now I wonder. Maybe true greatness can only be found by being in the world, among people, for all their flaws and foibles. - T

TEN OF CUPS

CONTENTMENT. LOVE. PERFECTION OF *the heart. Alignment with self and source.*

I was skimming through TV channels the other night, and an advertisement blared on the screen: "What's your best day?"

The Ten of Cups was my best day. It wasn't anything dramatic. Just the realization that I'd become the person I wanted to be. I was running a tea and Tarot room (okay, co-running it with my business partner, Abigail). I was in a great relationship, and I knew it wouldn't blow up for some stupid reason because I wasn't the guy who did stupid reasons anymore. I'd worked, and I'd grown, and I'd become the guy who *deserved* to be in a great relationship.

Will I keep changing and growing? I hope so. I think humans are like sharks. If we don't keep moving forward, we stagnate and die (metaphorically). Am I perfect? Of course not. But in that moment, I realized I'd leveled up, and where I was in that moment was *right*.

The Symbols

In this card, a happy family celebrates beneath a rainbow, a traditional symbol of good fortune, protection, and perfection. It's also a symbol of the connection between heaven and earth. The red roof of a house, a symbol of the self, security, and family, peeks from the woods in the background.

Like the Ten of Pentacles, the Ten of Cups promises good things. As a ten card, it's an ending of one life stage with a promise of more to come. But while the Pentacles are about physical reality, the Cups work in the realm of the psyche and emotions.

This Tarot card is about our inner state. And since the inner state affects the outer, these positive feelings pour over into our "real" lives as well.

But this card also asks us to consider our future "leveled up" life. How do we want to feel when we get there? This is an important question. So often we're focused on what success looks like, but not how it will make us feel. You may have heard the advice to act like the person you want to be? *Feeling* like that person is just as important when it comes to achieving your life goals. And if, as you move toward your goals, you're not feeling like that person, you might want to ask why.

What Does This Card Mean for You?

Are your goals out of alignment? Or are *you* out of alignment with your goals?[1]

---

1. I'm embarrassed. You've shamed me. I've been taming squirrels and navel-gazing instead of dealing with my father's murder. As awkward and incompetent as my detecting may be, I need to press on. And now you've also made me examine my motives. Why try to solve my father's murder? For justice? For myself? For him? I don't know. I just know now I have to try. I can't leave my fate or justice in the hands of others. - T

PAGE of CUPS.

PAGE OF CUPS

ROMANCE. A MAGICAL FLOW *state. Innocence. Intuition. An open, vulnerable heart.*

"It happened again." My friend Maureen walked into my office laughing and tossed a chic pair of sunglasses on my reading table. "Glasses this time. My cousin left them at my house. When I offered to mail them to her, she told me to keep 'em."

I knew *what happened again* wasn't someone losing things at Maureen's place. For the last two months, the universe had been showering her with gifts. She'd received everything from a juicer to a snowplow. (She lives in the Sierras, so the latter actually would come in handy).

When I asked Maureen what had changed her, she had no idea. She'd entered a flow state. Her heart was spilling over with love and goodwill, and people were responding. New romance had come into her life along with the random gifts. Work opportunities had opened up. She'd become the Page of Cups.

"I saw him," she said, "and it was like I'd been shot by Cupid's arrow. I'm still not sure if that's for real, or just a trick of Cupid."

I'm pretty sure it's for real, because I'd never seen *her* so real and raw, so happy and authentic. And even if it didn't work out, I knew something even better was just around the corner. For people filled with that much love, something always is.

The Symbols

In this odd little Tarot card, a youthful page with a wave-shaped hat holds a cup. A fish (representing the subconscious and premonitions) emerges from it, as if about to tell him a secret. A pearl centered on the Page's hat is evocative of the third eye, symbolizing intuition and psychic ability. His tunic is covered in tulips, symbols of love.

Taken together, this card represents a time when magical energies occur innocently, as parts of everyday life. It can also be a time when the qualities of this page—innocence, playfulness, enthusiasm, and vulnerability—are in play. (It took me a long time to realize that expressing vulnerability isn't always a weakness—not when it comes from a place of authenticity and confidence).

The turbulent waves and cocky confidence of the page's posture do present a warning, however. Youth and inexperience can sometimes take things too far.[1]

---

1. The squirrel got into a half-finished wine glass I'd left on the counter and vomited all over my laptop. Ugh. Worried he might have a latent vino allergy, I took him to the local vet.

  Though the vet's an older man, he's got one of those twinkly, innocent, young-at-heart vibes. My sister with all her animal rescues is one of his most frequent clients. So despite the late hour, he welcomed me warmly and examined the squirrel.

  Not a wine allergy. A ketamine overdose. He recognized the symptoms fairly quickly. Apparently he uses ketamine as an anesthetic, delivered by injection. I can't tell you how sick I felt as the vet described the symptoms. When taken orally, it can cause vomiting, dizziness, a sense of detachment from reality, hallucinations, and lost time. Sound familiar? Does this explain my so-called visions? It must, but I don't want to believe it. Someone's been spiking my wine. - T

What Does This Card Mean for You?

Can you trust that something wonderful is around the corner if you're fully alive and present to it? Because magic is at your fingertips. All you have to do is open your heart.

KNIGHT of CUPS.

KNIGHT OF CUPS

A MESSENGER. SENSITIVE. ROMANTIC. *Emotionally immature.*

My barber is in love with love. He falls into love harder and more easily than anyone I know, and then he regales the entire barbershop with tales of his latest date. And when he takes a woman out, he pulls out all the stops.

Which is why the last time I went in for a cut, he was hobbling around on crutches. He'd taken his newest love hang gliding.

"This one's for real," he assured me, brandishing his shears.

I'd heard that one before.

The Symbols

The Knight's winged helmet and shoes are reminiscent of Mercury, father of Cupid,[1] bringer of messages, and the planet associated with the Magician.

The Knight holds a cup before him and rides a white horse. It's an image reminiscent of a knight on a grail quest. This is a person who's searching.

---

1. This may confuse people. Cicero claimed Mercury was the father of Cupid, but other myths say differently. - T

But if ever a knight wore his heart on his sleeve, it's the Knight of Cups. The water imagery–particularly the fish on his tunic–symbolizes his watery emotional and spiritual nature, which is why many modern interpretations emphasize the Knight's sensitivity. And like all knights he's still a bit immature, sometimes making him overly emotional, temperamental, and given to flights of fancy.

What Does This Card Mean for You?

This knight is a visionary on a journey to the heart. Where is your heart taking you? What vision are you following?

QUEEN OF CUPS

IN THE FLOW. INTUITIVE. *Compassionate. Caring.*

"I was doing Gestalt consulting at a hospital." The man leaned back on the garden bench and laced his hands over his broad stomach. He was unprepossessing, with an egg-shaped head. Sunlight gleamed off his bald spot. "No one wanted to participate. Some of the doctors were downright hostile." He chuckled. "So I told them I got paid whether they participated or not, and I just waited. They came around."

We were staying at the same B&B, and I was fascinated by the man. He was completely in the flow, at ease with himself and life. It's difficult to describe the sense of peace I felt in his presence.

That afternoon in the garden he taught me a simple meditation technique. Eyes closed, for one minute, he had me concentrate on what I could feel—the clothing on my body, the pressure of my body in the chair, the breeze on my skin—but without labeling any of those feelings. Then, for another minute I focused on what I could smell—again no labels. Then what I could taste, then hear. Finally, he asked me to open my eyes, and note where I saw the color red, but not to label anything.

He never explained the technique, and I never asked. Years later, I realized he was teaching me to be aware, out of my head, and in the present moment.

He reminded me of the Queen of Cups on her best days—compassionate, caring, intuitive, and in the flow of life.

The Symbols

The Queen of Cups, seated in her throne by the shore, intently studies the elaborate[1] cup in her hands. Like the High Priestess, her robe dissolves into the water of emotions and intuition lapping at her feet.

She's a queen, so she's in charge. But she doesn't order or command. She simply *is*, and because of her benign presence, people have a hard time *not* falling in line around her.

I'd like to be more like her, but the truth is I spend too much time in my head and not enough just *being*. Too often, I'm the Queen of Cups on a bad day, too busy staring into her cup navel-gazing. And sometimes her compassion can turn smothering.

What Does This Card Mean for You?

This card asks us to consider how we can bring the positive qualities of the Queen of Cups to bear on a situation. Can you be more nurturing, loving, and empathetic?

---

1. Rosicrucian symbols on the cup include the Rose Cross on the stem and its peaked shape, the latter which is a symbol for the grave of magister temple, the third highest rank in the Rosicrucian order, and which is associated with the third Sephira, the mother. The cross represents the exoteric form of Christianity. And the cup's lion, eagle and bull plus the two angels on the handles may represent the hermetic elements or the four fixed signs of the zodiac. This queen's cup is big magic. - T

KING _{of} CUPS.

KING OF CUPS

DIPLOMATIC. TOLERANT. RESPONSIBLE. EMOTIONAL *control.*

A friend of mine took on an abandoned child—his granddaughter. I can only imagine how it must have felt—the disappointment in his daughter, who'd walked away, compounded with the sympathetic ache of raising an emotionally wounded child.

But he never let on, focusing instead on giving his granddaughter the support she needed. Now that emotionally wounded child is a healthy and happy adult.

He's still circumspect about the entire affair, not wanting to poison his granddaughter against his daughter any further. The only emotion I've seen him express about his family is joy and pride in his granddaughter and a mild sadness over his wayward daughter. He's a King of Cups kind of man.

The Symbols

As master of his emotions, the King feels things—sometimes quite deeply. Beneath his throne we see turbulent waters. But his feet don't touch them—he doesn't let his emotions flood his life.

The lotuses on his crown, scepter, and throne are symbols of beauty, purity, and serenity growing from contaminated or sullied beginnings. The King doesn't repress his emotions; he manages them, turning them to the good. He's in charge. And though he has desires, he's not attached to the outcomes.

His throne is on a stone platform, a stable foundation of wisdom, experience, and knowledge. He's mature, because he's a king, and he's also responsible. All these things make him a terrific diplomat.

But there's always a dark side. Ill-aspected, this diplomacy can turn to manipulation.[1]

What Does This Card Mean for You?

Like this king, you don't have to be blown about by emotions or situations. How can you find your base and stay steady rather than react?[2]

---

1. Or he can represent a seducer. - T

2. Did you know the King of Cups AND the Death card are associated with Scorpio? Scorpio's a fixed water sign, and its classical ruler (i.e. before later planets such as Pluto were discovered, and yes, Pluto IS still a freaking planet) was Mars, (sex and death?). Its modern ruler, Pluto, is connected with Judgment.

   I confronted Charles about the ketamine. He denied it, of course. What nearly sent me over the edge was he was so damned sympathetic about it all. He's treating me like I really am mentally wounded, and we haven't even gone to court over the conservatorship yet. I figured he was just practicing for the trial.   And then he told me the truth. He knows about my voluntary commitment five years ago. Adelaide once let it slip. He knows, and so does his lawyer, no doubt.

   That conniving, duplicitous bastard. - T

THE SUIT OF WANDS

FIRE
  Passion
  Will
  Heat
  Energy[1]

---

1. It inspires and destroys. - T

ACE OF WANDS

POTENTIAL. CREATION. INVENTION. A *beginning*.

Abigail still hasn't forgiven me for setting off that firework in the tearoom last Chinese New Year. In fairness, it was an accident (I really thought it was a dud). It also nearly took my eyebrows off.

But the minor explosion was also useful. That blast of colored light didn't just illuminate the hallway, it illuminated *me*. In a flash, I realized that the excitement of expanding my Tarot business and partnering in the tearoom had faded because I'd *done* it. My business had expanded. And maybe... that's why I was being a tiny bit reckless with the New Year fireworks.

I needed a new Tarot project to get excited about. Abigail and I had built something truly magical at Beanblossom's. But I realized I could do more.

And suddenly, *I knew what to do*. It was time to write my book on Tarot. My burst of insight was the Ace of Wands.

The Symbols

The burning branch[1] being handed to you represents a flash of inspiration, the beginning of something new. Its sparks are shaped like *Yods*, the letter of the Hebrew alphabet that represents the starter, all that is, the first motion.

This is a call to fulfill potential, and the demand that you *do* it. It's not a sit-on-the-couch-and-expect-things-to-happen sort of card. The Ace of Wands is a get-off-your-duff-and-*make*-things happen card.

What Does This Card Mean for You?

Occasionally, clients come to me for a Tarot reading to try and understand who they are. But a better question is: who *could* they be? Because how many of us really are reaching our full potential?

I know I'm not. I could be studying a foreign language in my free time instead of doing tequila shots in that beachside bar.

Who could *you* be?[2]

---

1. It also means sexual attraction. Can that wand get any more phallic?

   What? You thought just because my life was crashing down on me I'd stop editing your manuscript? Nah. - T

2. There's a period in the potential mystic's life called the dark night of the soul. It's exactly what it sounds like. If you come out the other side (not all do), you may achieve union with the Divine. I felt a bit like that when I woke up this morning. Everything became... clear. There's a road ahead for me, and it doesn't involve being my brother's ward. I intend to do everything in my power to take this new path. - T

TWO OF WANDS

DREAMS. PLANNING. DOMINION. COURAGE.

My friend Razzzor, who's nowhere near as intimidating as his name sounds, dropped by the tearoom the other day and mentioned he had an idea for a computer game.

"Sounds cool," I said, though I'm not into gaming. "Are you going ahead with it?"

"I already have." Rocking back on his high-tops, he shoved his glasses higher up his nose. "Trademark's registered and the programmers are being hired."

I gaped in awe. There was no hesitation between his dream and his action. But I knew, since Razzzor is actually quite successful, that there *were* steps between the two, namely planning and organizing. In that great big brain of his they all just happen in rapid-fire, and *then* he acts.

I don't have those in-between steps. I dream, and then I dream some more, and *eventually* I'll act, but without a whole lot of thought. (This is why having a business partner who knows how to plan works well for me).

Razzzor is the guy in the Two of Wands, and I'm... not. But I'd like to be.

The Symbols

A well-dressed man stands on a castle parapet. He holds a globe in one hand and a staff in the other. The globe mirrors that in the Emperor card and represents the man's material power. He literally has the world in his hands.

Two wands form a gateway for him to gaze through, but the wands are both restricted — one is held by a clamp to the wall and the other is gripped in the man's hand.

Engraved in the lower-left corner of the wall are a crossed rose and lily. These two flowers are symbolic opposites, the rose representing desire and the lily purity. It's this crossing of opposites here that I believe is the key to this card: rose and lilies, water and mountains. The man's not just daydreaming, he's putting things into action. His dreams are moderated by plans and good sense.

What Does This Card Mean for You?

If this card appears in a reading, it's a sign you literally have the world in your hands. But are you fully living up to the potential the Two of Wands offers, going beyond dreams and into planning and action?[1]

---

1. Oh, I've got a plan all right. - T

THREE OF WANDS

ENTERPRISE. TAKING THE BROAD *or strategic view. Planning. Progress.*

Becoming part-owner in Beanblossom's Tea and Tarot was a massive leap of faith. I believed we'd succeed, but I didn't *know*. How could I?

Even more terrifying, I *wouldn't* know right off. Restaurants can take a year to get off the ground. Losses and slow starts are expected.

And though I wasn't running the food side, my Tarot business was knotted right into it. Either we both succeeded, or neither of us did.

So I took the leap, relying on the plans my partner and I had developed (I *did* help with those plans. A little.). And then I waited like the man on the Three of Wands, watching his ships sail into the distance and hoping to hell they'd make it back safely.

A year later, I still feel a bit like that man. Beanblossom's is doing well, but anything could happen. And all I can do is keep on keeping on and let the events we set in motion unfold on their own.

The Symbols

This card is filled with promise. The skies are clear. The hill is green. The three wands beside the man are budding. Depending on the situation, this card asks us to trust in the process and get back to work. After all, staring after those ships on the horizon won't do any good.

It also asks us to have courage. The man in the card is wearing armor beneath his robes (you can only see it on his exposed arm, but it's there). He's a fighter. And it can take courage after the act to trust and to wait.

What Does This Card Mean for You?

Consider how you relate to the man on the hill. The situation calls for planning, creativity, and some strategic visioning and understanding. Are you prepared?[1]

---

1. I haven't found any evidence to prove who killed my father. But it couldn't have been Joan or her driver. This leaves my loving siblings.

Means? It wouldn't have been hard for either to push him off that balcony if he'd been drinking. Motive? Charles and Adelaide have plenty. Opportunity? Ditto.

The key is the ketamine. Only one person had the means, motive, and opportunity to spike my wine. And this means that same person planned my frame-up and the murder in advance.

If the fire hadn't driven me from my cabin, if I hadn't returned home, would my father still be alive? I can't think about that, though I still feel it. I'll feel it for a long time, I suspect. I tweaked my plan to get the evidence I need. I'm not going to rush into things and make a mistake. Too much rides on my success. - T

Four of Wands

CELEBRATION. BALANCE. FULFILLMENT. COMPLETION.

My grandfather owned a hardware store. Every morning, he'd get up at five AM, meet his buddies for coffee, then open the shop. And every evening, he'd be home by seven. And long past the age when he could have sold out and retired, he kept working.

Once I asked him why he didn't cash out. His routine seemed brutally boring. He just smiled. "When you find something you love," he said, "you don't quit."

For most of my life, I was happy being the lone wolf. I didn't want anyone to hold me down, and I was *happy*. I liked my life. I liked my solo Tarot practice. I *liked* being able to play the field.

And then I met the right people, and everything changed. It threw me in a way I didn't want to admit. I began to question my life and my choices. I told myself I didn't *need* a business partner to succeed or to be in a committed relationship to be happy. I'd been fine before without either. But I was having a harder time believing it. Now I can't imagine living any other way, or with any other people.

I finally understood what my grandfather was talking about.

The Symbols

In this card, a garlanded couple celebrates between a walled city and two pairs of wands. There's a bridge in the background—a symbol for a path between two worlds. The bridge also represents the ability to overcome whatever stands between those worlds. This makes the Four of Wands a particularly hopeful card. The celebration is coming into being.

What Does This Card Mean for You?

Get ready. How can you cultivate the positive emotions to receive the coming blessing?[1]

---

1. The time has not come. So thanks again for this editing project. It's keeping my mind occupied.

Fours are associated with structure, foundation, and the physical universe. The Four of Wands is associated with Mercy (Chesed) on the Kabbalah's Tree of Life. Chesed's triangle is a reflection of the supernal triangle, the first reflection, and some have surmised that the fours therefore think they're twos—which may hold for the Four of Wands as the wands appear to be reflections of each other. So it might be worthwhile to look at what two represents: duality, balance, and choice. I think of this as the couple card, and if you're a part of one, asking how you can support and celebrate your other half.

The card also corresponds with the Decan of Venus (associated with the Empress) in Aries (associated with the Emperor and Mars). So astrologically, this represents the beginnings of new, exciting energy and opportunities.

Are you excited, Hyperion? I am. - T

FIVE OF WANDS

CONFLICT. PROBLEMS. COMPETITION. MAKING *mountains out of molehills.*

I have (or had) an arch nemesis. He was always one-upping me. Well, more like ten-upping me. He was hugely successful. I hate to admit that it made me crazy.

But here's the thing. He also spurred me to work harder, go deeper, take more risks. And though at the time I felt like he was making my life harder, he wasn't, not really. He made it better.

Competition can go too far. But the whole point of competing in sports is that competition pushes us to be our very best. It can do that in life too.

The Symbols

Which brings us to the Five of Wands. Fives represent instability, challenges, upsetting the balance.[1] Five can also represent freedom, change, and adventure. In short, there's a lot of energy in this Tarot card.

We see five youths whacking each other with oversized, budding staffs. And while the chaos has the potential for black eyes and wounded egos, it's not a serious battle. In fact, AE Waite specified it can symbolize an "imitation" or "sham fight."

When this card appears in a reading, it could indicate a conflict isn't about what you think it is, and it might not be real at all. It may well be much ado about nothing. And if handled correctly, it may make you better and stronger.

What Does This Card Mean for You?

How is conflict operating in your life? Is it helping, or hurting, or blown out of proportion?[2]

---

1. As most odd numbers are, five is a "masculine" number. Astrological associations: Saturn in Leo. Leo's a fire sign (as the Wands are fire cards), and it's generous, bold, and courageous. In its negative aspect, Leo can be arrogant, bossy, swaggering, and self-centered. At the spiritual level, Leo embodies the energy of risk and rules self-expression, gambling, and creativity. Perhaps the willingness to be completely alive is the ultimate gamble. Or perhaps it only feels that way, and to do the opposite means a wasted life. Saturn, on the other hand, is the planet of structure and order, defining our limits. Leo shows the energy, risk, and liveliness of the Five of Wands, while Saturn demonstrates its drive and force of will.   - T

2. I went to my father's house today but was spotted and had to retreat. The betrayal stings, Hyperion. It stings. I thought I was better than this. I thought I was above it. What has happened to me? - T

SIX OF WANDS

SUCCESS. RECOGNITION. GRATITUDE.

I don't know any professional Tarot readers who hung out their shingle and immediately started rolling in dough. When I got started, my earnings were lean. Practically skeletal, in fact. There was a lot of scrambling and stressing and striving.

When I finally partnered up to found Beanblossom's Tea and Tarot, I exchanged one set of challenges for another. Now I had to worry about my budget affecting others, about managing Tarot readers, and about pulling my weight so we could make the rent.

A funny thing happened. We were successful, but I didn't know it.

I was so used to the grind that struggle had become my mindset. Then I was invited to a prestigious Tarot conference. I was thrilled. I'd be a speaker! Rubbing elbows with other Tarotistas!

I'm embarrassed to say that invitation is what made me finally look around and realize... we'd made it. Beanblossom's was a success. I had everything I'd wanted—the freedom to set my schedule, money to pay the bills and then some, friends and family, and even some recognition from the Tarot world.

And I'd wasted *months* not enjoying any of it.

The Symbols

The Six of Wands shows a triumphal procession. A man on horseback wears a laurel crown and is cheered on by the crowd. This Tarot card's divinatory message is success and recognition, and in certain positions, it could mean a message on the way. But generally speaking, it explores the phenomena of success, and how we handle it.

What Does This Card Mean for You?

You can be proud of your achievements. Have you stopped to recognize how far you've come and to celebrate?[1]

---

1. Success! I've GOT her. I'm safe now. But the victory... I can't even say it's bittersweet. It has no taste, bitter or sweet. I should be phoning the cops now. I'll tell them, of course. I have to. But this family...

   I don't want to see any of them again. I should have stayed in my cabin in the woods and risked the fire. What happened was my fault. I see it now. If I'd been true to myself, I never would have slunk home to this life of ease. Slumming it in a caretaker's cottage on a massive estate? What a joke. I betrayed myself by coming here. Is it any wonder things went so wrong? - T

SEVEN OF WANDS

Moral superiority. Courage of *convictions. Challenge. Defense. Perseverance.*

When I was in high school, I saw a kid being bullied. The first time it happened, I did nothing and told myself it was none of my business. The second time, I did nothing and felt ashamed. The third time, I stepped in , and I became the bully's focus of abuse for the next six months.

I didn't enjoy being a target. But I didn't mind it as much as I thought I would either. Being bullied felt better than the shame I'd felt when I hadn't gotten involved.

It was my first Seven of Wands moment.

The Symbols

In the card, a man stands on high ground. He uses a budding staff to defend against six other staffs.

The defender's shoes are mismatched. This could represent being off-balance, a sudden attack (which caused him to grab whatever footwear was nearest at hand), or being of two minds. Water trickles from beneath his booted foot, also symbolizing an "unbalanced" position.

Water can also indicate the subconscious or emotions. The defender may have the high ground, but there's a certain instability to it.

We don't see the people he's fighting—only the attacking staffs. The attackers aren't the point in this card. It's the defense that matters. Or perhaps there are no attackers, and the battle is all taking place in the querent's mind?

What Does This Card Mean for You?

Goodness and beauty are worth defending. What are you fighting for?[1]

2

---

1. The Seven of Wands is associated with Mars in Leo, which indicates a lot of brashness and forceful energy. Mars, the Roman god of War, is associated with the disastrous Tower card. The planet's reddish color is associated with anger. Yet, Mars can also

2. Note from Hyperion: This is the last edit I received from T. He seems to have emailed me the manuscript before finishing. I can only assume he was interrupted.

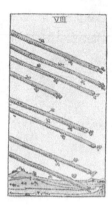

EIGHT OF WANDS

SWIFT MOVEMENT. ACTIVITY. GOOD *news. (And the occasional check in the mail).*

Not only does my business partner, Abigail, have an uncanny ability to know exactly which envelope will contain a check, she can seemingly echolocate the envelopes as well.

I once misplaced an envelope with a very nice check in it somewhere in my office. She found me tearing through my desk drawer in a hapless fury. When I told her the problem, she turned in place, pressed her finger to her nose (I kid you not), then pointed at a box full of business envelopes I'd bought for my own mailings. She strolled over to it and pulled out the envelope with my check. I must have dropped it in there by mistake.

This would be a much more exciting superpower if checks weren't going the way of the dodo.

But.

This is all a way of working into the Eight of Wands. Because Abigail's swift, unerring action was *totally* an Eight of Wands power move, (especially with the big money ending).

The Symbols

The Eight of Wands depicts eight wands bulleting through the air. This is a card of movement at speed. The way is clear. Things are happening. Energy is moving.

What Does This Card Mean for You?

The Eight of Wands can be a call for you to act swiftly and decisively, or... it can mean someone or something else is moving fast and will impact you—possibly directly in the chest. Those reversed cards can be painful, especially when they're not a simple diminishment of the card's meaning.

Things may be moving more quickly than expected. What action do you need to take to prepare or to make sure things go your way?

Nine of Wands

Resilience. Persistence. Healthy boundaries. *Courage. Determination.*

"I've been ghosted." My business partner Abigail dropped into the highbacked chair opposite, her checked apron flouncing about her hips. She huffed a breath.

"What?" I asked, indignant. "By whom? How?"

She groaned. "Everything seemed to be going so well. We had fun together. We had similar values. He seemed totally into me. And then, poof. Gone."

We commiserated, and I halfheartedly volunteered to help with the cleanup in the tearoom that night. We both knew she'd never accept, but it made her smile.

Once she got beyond feeling like hot garbage, she realized the loser had done her a favor. They hadn't been right for each other for many reasons. Later, she admitted she'd known it from the start but had let herself revel in the romantic fantasy anyway.

The ghosting ended up being a wakeup call. She'd tricked herself into falling for a relationship that wasn't right, but why? Once she dug deeper into that why, she saw the root of the problem and dug it out.

And she felt... battered. Yes, we both knew she'd come through it and would be fine—better than she was before, in fact. But that sort of thing is always exhausting. It was very Nine of Wands.

The Symbols

In the card, a man with a bandaged head leans on a staff and surveys eight other staffs, arranged like a protective barrier around him. Since this is a nine, representing endings, the fight is over—for now, at least.

But this character's still looking a little wary. After all, there's a lot that can get through those wands. But maybe that's a good thing? We don't want to become too hardened, too defensive, or we'll keep out all the good experiences too.

What Does This Card Mean for You?

But let's get back to that nine and the good news. It's over. Now... What steps do you need to take to pick yourself up and carry on?

TEN OF WANDS

AN ENDING IS NEAR. *Struggle. Oppression. The need for change.*

A client came to me feeling burned out. She'd worked her entire life and was successful in her field—not at the top of it, but comfortably successful. She had an amazing house, and the mortgage was paid off. She owned her own company and was doing work she loved. She had a beloved family.

She was also tense and stressed and ready to crack. Her blood pressure was through the roof. She was prediabetic. She was not looking good. So it was no surprise that the Ten of Wands appeared in her reading.

The Symbols

The card shows a man carrying a bundle of ten staffs. He shambles toward a nearby village. His back is bent. The staffs are clearly weighing on him, which is why this card often is associated with struggle and oppression.

But here's the thing. Look at how he's holding the sticks in *front* of him. He could make his life easier and carry them on his back or shoulder, but instead, he's chosen the most awkward position possible.

The sticks are also right in front of his face, so it's unclear if he can see how close he is to reaching the village, where he can set them down. In short, the struggle may be real, but it doesn't have to be this tough. This guy needs to make some changes.

So did my client. She'd spent so many years working flat out, she was driving herself into an early grave. Her habit, her mindset, was go-go-go. But it was time for her to ease up before she had a heart attack.

Once she did, her life transformed. She began taking more time for leisure and to take care of her health, which she'd been neglecting. She got her blood pressure under control and moved out of the pre-diabetic category.

What Does This Card Mean for You?

Sometimes, a portion of our burdens are of our own making. What blockages—internal or external—might there be to releasing the burdens you carry?

PAGE of WANDS.

Page of Wands

CREATIVITY. INSPIRATION. POTENTIAL. YOUTHFUL *confidence. Free spirit.*

My mother wrangled me into helping clean out their garage. While hefting dusty crates hither and yon, I found an old cardboard box from my teenage days. Inside was an early book on Tarot I'd written.

It was *terrible.* I'd sold it at a loss to my friends.

Part of me couldn't bear perusing this blast from the past. The other part was fascinated by how far I'd come—both in writing style and in my understanding of Tarot.

I'd put a lot of work into that book, with its thick, black paper cover I'd handbound with a saddle stitch. I'd used heavy paper my parents had brought back from Italy at my request. The edges of the cream pages were uneven—the paper had been handmade in a 13th century paper mill. The soft, textured paper even had a heraldic watermark to add an aura of the occult and esoteric. It was clumsy art, made by a young man who didn't really know what he was doing but was trying hard.

Was it professional? No. Would I let *any* of my clients read it? *Hell* no.

But it was a start. And if I hadn't made the leap, if I hadn't had the nerve to put it out into the world, if I hadn't struggled to write my thoughts down—half confused as they were—would I be writing this book today?

The Symbols

This Page stands in a desert. He gazes off the card and holds a wand budding with leaves. On a more mundane level, his body language suggests a "town crier" or herald, which reflects the Arthur Edward Waite interpretation of the Page of Wands being a bearer of strange tidings.

The symbolism on the Page of Wands is all earth (the metal helmet, the sand dunes), fire (the yellow and red clothing, the salamanders on his tunic, the red plume on helmet), and youth. Earth symbolizes making things manifest—this page is a doer. Fire speaks to action, passion, and idealism. And youth represents the start of things, beginnings, immaturity, naivete.

But sometimes we need a dose of naivete to just jump in, even if we don't quite know what we're doing. After all, doing is the best way to learn. Is it time to bring this Page into your life?

What Does This Card Mean for You?

Like all Court Cards, the page can represent a quality within you acting on the situation, a quality you should bring to the situation, or someone else involved in the situation.

This card is offering an opportunity for passion, adventure, and excitement—the opportunity to make your dreams a reality. What's exciting you now? Where do your passions lie?

KNIGHT of WANDS.

KNIGHT OF WANDS

INSPIRED ACTION. FREE SPIRIT. *Impetuosity. Confidence. Making change.*

My client Paul came into my office in a slump. He was in his mid-fifties and fairly successful. But he wasn't happy.

"Is this the midlife crisis?" He collapsed in the high-backed chair opposite. "I just keep questioning everything I've done and not done. Was it worth it? Have I lost my chance? I'm at the stage in life where there's less in front of me than behind me. Where more is being taken from me than given. More than I can give."

"That's not true," I said, shuffling the deck.

"Isn't it? Nothing I've done or will do matters. A hundred years from now, I won't even be a footnote in history. I'll just be gone."

"Does it matter?" I asked.

"What do you mean?"

"Does it matter that nothing you do, no matter how impressive, will make a damn bit of difference long-term?"

"Thanks." He laughed hollowly. "You're making me feel *much* better."

Ignoring the sarcasm, I drew a card and turned it over. It was the Knight of Wands reversed.

"Let's say you're right," I said. "Which FYI, I don't believe. What we do may go unnoted, but it does matter. Our actions have a ripple effect, and we can't know what the impacts will be downstream. I mean, look at Marcus Aurellius."

"Who?"

"Ancient Roman emperor. He wrote the *Meditations*. They were his personal notes, reminding himself to be a good person. He didn't expect them to be shared after his death. But today, they inspire millions to live good lives. This little, good thing he did, just to improve himself, has rippled outward."

Bad actions have the same ripple effect, alas. But Paul was a good man. I knew he'd take this in the right direction and put good things out into the world. "But let's say it's true that our tiny efforts don't matter. If that's true, why not go where your energy leads you? Stop dwelling and follow what excites you."

"You're saying I'm overthinking this?"

I tapped the upside-down card. "I'm saying this guy wouldn't let doubts get in the way. And this Knight's definitely not done. He is being blocked though, and I think we know what's holding him back."

Paul nodded slowly. "I'm holding myself back."

The Knight of Wands is hard-charging, impetuous, bold. Paul needed to bring that energy back into his life, even if he wasn't really feeling it.

The Symbols

The Knight's rearing horse is a symbol for restless energy, movement, and change. We can see other clues to the Knight's personality in what he's wearing. Fire-like feathers ripple from the top of his helmet and the joints of his armor, implying creative rather than just raw physical energy. The Knight's mantle is torn—he's been in battle.

Like the other knights, he wears armor, representing ideals, visions, and noble intentions. Also like the other Knights, he corresponds with fire. So does the suit of Wands, making this a double-fire card. There's a lot of heat in this Knight, and if you sense a double entendre here, you're right.

This fiery Knight is ready to *go*.

What Does This Card Mean for You?

As with all Court Cards, consider if the energies of the Knight of Wands are helping or hurting the situation.

What would you like to change right now? Because it may be time to seize the moment. You'll be most successful in your endeavor if you embody the qualities of this knight—optimism, action, and adventure.

But beware. Passion can burn out quickly if it's not properly nurtured.

QUEEN OF WANDS

INDEPENDENT. HONORABLE. SOCIABLE. CONFIDENT. *Dynamic.*

Every October, I buy an antique Halloween postcard. I prefer the cards that have been used, because I like reading other people's mail.

Don't judge.

And I suppose the fact that these old postcards remind me of Tarot cards has something to do with my interest. One of my favorites depicts a cheeky Gibson girl holding a witch's broom. Substitute the broomstick for a wand, and you've got Queen of Wands material. This queen's got power.

The Symbols

The Queen of Wands holds a sunflower in one hand and a wand as a scepter in the other. These flowers symbolize solar energy and nature at its fullest. As a side note, the Greek word for sunflower is Clytie, which means "famous one." This queen is no shrinking violet.

Her throne is decorated with lions (representing Leo and the fire element). She wears a leopard brooch. A black cat—a domesticated version of the wild cat and a symbol of magic and goddess worship—sits at her feet.

The queen looks off to the left, symbolizing the subconscious, femininity, and receptivity. She's also looking away from her Wand, as if there are other things going on in her life.

Like all queens in Tarot, she has a soft power. Hers is the power to bewitch and bedazzle. The Queen of Wands is the woman who makes you not only feel at home when you arrive at a party knowing no one, but she also makes you feel like the star of the night. And being a queen, she gets stuff *done*.

But taken too far, these energies can turn dark. *Sociable* can become reckless party girl. Independence can become isolation. Honor can become ideology. If this card is reversed, you need to ask yourself how these energies are in play, or if the queen's positive energies are being repressed somehow.

What Does This Card Mean for You?

And now, even though I'm really not feeling it, I'm off to a Halloween party. Because the Queen of Wands isn't the sort of girl to sit at home with a good book. She calls us to get out there and *mingle*.

This card reminds us that life is short. If we're not having fun, we're doing it wrong.

Take some time to consider how you're feeling about yourself. How can you incorporate the positive aspects of the Queen of Wands into your life?

KING of WANDS

KING OF WANDS

Vision. Passion. Honesty. *A leader or entrepreneur.*

When I first met my now business partner, Abigail, she had a business plan for a tearoom complete with fabric swatches and five-year financial projections.

I had... a scrap of paper and lots of ideas. Neither of our plans worked out as we'd expected.

They turned out *better.*

That's not to bash planning. If we didn't have any plans, we wouldn't have been able to toss them in the air, modify them, and create Bean-blossom's Tea and Tarot room. Okay, Abigail did all the modifying. The point is, it *worked.*

As I write this at the beginning of a new year, she's busily scribbling in her planner and devising goals and setting budgets. I think it's kind of fun and charming.

But I'm not a planner. I *do* believe in imagining the outcome you want. I may not have a plan, but I have a *vision.* Together, Abigail and I are the King of Wands. I've got the vision; she creates step-by-step tasks and goals. In short, the King of Wands is the whole package, even if on my own, I'm not.

The Symbols

This card is littered with symbols for the element of fire, from the salamanders to the flame-like crown, and lions. The King leans forward in his throne, as if he's ready to stand and take action.

He's a responsible person, both because he's a king and because beneath his crown he wears a heraldic red "cap of maintenance," which is a symbol of social responsibility and care for his kingdom.

What Does This Card Mean for You?

As with all Court Cards, the King of Wands can represent a person you know or energies or attributes that you need to activate in your life. But now is the time to act.

In my case... I probably should do a *little* more work on the nitty-gritty of planning so I can achieve my big vision.

How are the King's energies operating (or not) in your life? Are you leading with passion and honesty? Is it time to step out and turn that side hustle into a bona fide business? Are you planning without vision? Visioning without planning? It's never too late to start.

EPILOGUE

TOM HASN'T RESPONDED TO my emails. Needless to say, after that visit from the authorities, I've watched the news carefully.

Adelaide was arrested for the murder of her father and for starting the fire that scorched hundreds of acres and burned the caretaker's cottage to the ground. There were no details on how, exactly, the fire started. They're probably saving that for the trial. The speculation is that she couldn't wait to inherit and decided to speed her father's death along.

I hear she has an excellent lawyer. She's out on bail and may remain so for years. Her animal charity won't suffer though. Her brother Charles is funding it through profits from their father's companies, which he is apparently running with aplomb.

Tom's disappeared, but I can't believe he's gone. I like to think he'll get in touch, that he's vanished to a different cabin in a different woods. That he isn't done.

After all, in Tarot, endings are also beginnings. The last card in each suit is like the first card, the Fool, taking a leap of faith and initiating new beginnings from old endings.

And that's not just wishful thinking. I received an odd postcard yesterday. It had been slipped beneath the door at Beanblossom's.

Considering Tom's father, there's been a lot of press around this crime. Hoaxers are everywhere, and more than a few have reached out to me.

Am I imagining this postcard is from Tom? Am I seeing what I want to see? It read:

Maybe those Renaissance artists understood that life in the end is much like a game. We may not hold all the cards. Others may have better hands.

But there are strategies which will improve our odds of winning. And that is TaroT.

Numerological Symbols

ZERO: NOTHINGNESS. PURE POTENTIAL.

One: Beginnings, creation, ideas, will. The active, male principal, initiation, inspiration and aspiration – that which is about to take form

Two: Duality, balance, choice. The number two also symbolizes assimilation and envisioning, as well as the relationship between two objects, ideas, or people.

Three: Expression, creation, fertilization, growth. The first manifestation of something real and supportive. Manifesting what we desire through work with others.

Four: Structure, foundation, and the physical universe. Fours bring different aspects of energy together working as one, but it doesn't stay stable—the four energy wants to keep moving, expanding.

Five: Instability, upsetting the balance, challenges, difficulties, uncertainty, and a new cycle. Freedom, change, and adventure.

Six: Harmony within change, justice, equilibrium, fairness, peace.

Seven: Fate, divine order, wisdom. Spiritual development, divine justice, change, rebellion, eccentricity, intuition, the completion of a phase or cycle.

Eight: Stability, spiritual strength, power, balance, and control. New ways forward, or new directions.

Nine: Completion, nearing the end, attainment, and preparation for transition. Mysticism and dreams.

Ten: An ending with the possibility for transition.

MORE KIRSTEN WEISS

THE PERFECTLY PROPER PARANORMAL Museum Mysteries

When highflying Maddie Kosloski is railroaded into managing her small-town's paranormal museum, she tells herself it's only temporary... until a corpse in the museum embroils her in murders past and present.

If you love quirky characters and cats with attitude, you'll love this laugh-out-loud cozy mystery series with a light paranormal twist. It's perfect for fans of Jana DeLeon, Laura Childs, and Juliet Blackwell. Start with book 1, *The Perfectly Proper Paranormal Museum*, and experience these charming wine-country whodunits today.

The Tea & Tarot Cozy Mysteries

Welcome to Beanblossom's Tea and Tarot, where each and every cozy mystery brews up hilarious trouble.

Abigail Beanblossom's dream of owning a tearoom is about to come true. She's got the lease, the start-up funds, and the recipes. But Abigail's out of a tearoom and into hot water when her realtor turns out to be a conman... and then turns up dead.

Take a whimsical journey with Abigail and her partner Hyperion through the seaside town of San Borromeo (patron saint of heartburn sufferers). And be sure to check out the easy tearoom recipes in the back of each book! Start the adventure with book 1, *Steeped in Murder*.

The Wits' End Cozy Mysteries

Cozy mysteries that are out of this world...

Running the best little UFO-themed B&B in the Sierras takes organization, breakfasting chops, and a talent for turning up trouble.

The truth is out there... Way out there in these hilarious whodunits. Start the series and beam up book 1, *At Wits' End*, today!

Pie Town Cozy Mysteries

When Val followed her fiancé to coastal San Nicholas, she had ambitions of starting a new life and a pie shop. One broken engagement later, at least her dream of opening a pie shop has come true.... Until one of her regulars keels over at the counter.

Welcome to Pie Town, where Val and pie-crust specialist Charlene are baking up hilarious trouble. Start this laugh-out-loud cozy mystery series with book 1, *The Quiche and the Dead.*

A Big Murder Mystery Series

Small Town. Big Murder.

The number one secret to my success as a bodyguard? Staying under the radar. But when a wildly public disaster blew up my career and reputation, it turned my perfect, solitary life upside down.

I thought my tiny hometown of Nowhere would be the ideal out-of-the-way refuge to wait out the media storm.

It wasn't.

My little brother had moved into a treehouse. The obscure mountain town had decided to attract tourists with the world's largest collection of big things... Yes, Nowhere now has the world's largest pizza cutter. And lawn flamingo. And ball of yarn...

And then I stumbled over a dead body.

All the evidence points to my brother being the bad guy. I may have been out of his life for a while—okay, five years—but I know he's no killer. Can I clear my brother before he becomes Nowhere's next Big Fatality?

A fast-paced and funny cozy mystery series, start with Big Shot.

The Doyle Witch Mysteries

In a mountain town where magic lies hidden in its foundations and forests, three witchy sisters must master their powers and shatter a curse before it destroys them and the home they love.

This thrilling witch mystery series is perfect for fans of Annabel Chase, Adele Abbot, and Amanda Lee. If you love stories rich with packed with magic, mystery, and murder, you'll love the Witches of Doyle. Follow the magic with the Doyle Witch trilogy, starting with book 1, *Bound.*

The Riga Hayworth Paranormal Mysteries

Her gargoyle's got an attitude.

Her magic's on the blink.

Alchemy might be the cure... if Riga can survive long enough to puzzle out its mysteries.

All Riga wants is to solve her own personal mystery—how to rebuild her magical life. But her new talent for unearthing murder keeps getting in the way...

If you're looking for a magical page-turner with a complicated, 40-something heroine, read the paranormal mystery series that fans of Patricia Briggs and Ilona Andrews call AMAZING! Start your next adventure with book 1, *The Alchemical Detective*.

Sensibility Grey Steampunk Suspense

California Territory, 1848.

Steam-powered technology is still in its infancy.

Gold has been discovered, emptying the village of San Francisco of its male population.

And newly arrived immigrant, Englishwoman Sensibility Grey, is alone.

The territory may hold more dangers than Sensibility can manage. Pursued by government agents and a secret society, Sensibility must decipher her father's clockwork secrets, before time runs out.

If you love over-the-top characters, twisty mysteries, and complicated heroines, you'll love the Sensibility Grey series of steampunk suspense. Start this steampunk adventure with book 1, *Steam and Sensibility*.

GET KIRSTEN'S MOBILE APP

Keep up with the latest book news, and get free short stories, scone recipes and more by downloading Kirsten's mobile app.
Just click HERE to get started or use the QR code below.
Or make sure you're on Kirsten's email list to get your free copy of the Tea & Tarot mystery, *Fortune Favors the Grave.*
You can do that here: KirstenWeiss.com or use the QR code below:

Connect with Kirsten

You can download my free app here:

https://kirstenweissbooks.beezer.com

Or sign up for my newsletter and get a special digital prize pack for joining, including an exclusive Tea & Tarot novella, *Fortune Favors the Grave.*

https://kirstenweiss.com

Or maybe you'd like to chat with other whimsical mystery fans? Come join Kirsten's reader page on Facebook:

https://www.facebook.com/kirsten.weiss

Or... sign up for my read and review team on Booksprout:

https://booksprout.co/author/8142/kirsten-weiss

About the Author

I write laugh-out-loud, page-turning mysteries for people who want to escape with real, complex, and flawed but likable characters. If there's magic in the story, it must work consistently within the world's rules and be based in history or the reality of current magical practices.

I'm best known for my cozy mystery and witch mystery novels, though I've written some steampunk mystery as well. So if you like funny, action-packed mysteries with complicated heroines, just turn the page...

Learn more, grab my **free app**, or sign up for my **newsletter** for exclusive stories and book updates. I also have a read-and-review tea via **Booksprout** and is looking for honest and thoughtful reviews! If you're interested, download the **Booksprout app**, follow me on Booksprout, and opt-in for email notifications.

BB bookbub.com/profile/kirsten-weiss

g goodreads.com/author/show/5346143.Kirsten_Weiss

f facebook.com/kirsten.weiss

instagram.com/kirstenweissauthor/

CPSIA information can be obtained
at www.ICGtesting.com
Printed in the USA
JSHW081334120423
40227JS00002B/196